# HSC
### Health & Safety
### Commission

# Safety of pressure systems

## Pressure Systems Safety Regulations 2000

# APPROVED CODE OF PRACTICE

**L122**

HSE BOOKS

**Approved Code of Practice**

This Code has been approved by the Health and Safety Commission, with the consent of the Secretary of State. It gives practical advice on how to comply with the law. If you follow the advice you will be doing enough to comply with the law in respect of those specific matters on which the Code gives advice. You may use alternative methods to those set out in the Code in order to comply with the law.

However, the Code has a special legal status. If you are prosecuted for breach of health and safety law, and it is proved that you did not follow the relevant provisions of the Code, you will need to show that you have complied with the law in some other way or a court will find you at fault.

**Guidance and Guide**

The document also contains additional guidance and guide material approved by the Health and Safety Commission.

Following the guidance is not compulsory and you are free to take other action. But if you do follow the guidance you will normally be doing enough to comply with the law. Health and safety inspectors seek to secure compliance with the law and may refer to this guidance as illustrating good practice.

The text marked as guide sets out the law and explains what it means in simple terms.

# Contents

**Notice of Approval**

By virtue of section 16(1) of the Health and Safety at Work etc Act 1974, and with the consent of the Secretary of State for the Environment, Transport and the Regions, the Health and Safety Commission has on 14 February 2000 approved the Code of Practice entitled *Safe pressure systems.*

The Code of Practice is approved for the purposes of providing practical guidance with respect to the requirements of the Pressure Systems Safety Regulations. The Code of Practice comes into effect on 21 February 2000. With effect from that date *Safety of pressure systems* (COP37) ceases to have effect.

Signed

ROSEMARY BANNER
*Secretary to the Health and Safety Commission*

14 February 2000

## Preface

This publication contains the full text of the Regulations, guide (a simple explanation of the law), the Approved Code of Practice (ACOP) and guidance on the Pressure Systems Safety Regulations 2000 (SI 2000 No 128).

In this publication, the Pressure Systems Safety Regulations 2000 are shown in *italic* type. The Approved Code of Practice is shown in **bold** type. The remaining text, in normal type, is additional guide and guidance on the subject.

The formal status of ACOP, guide and guidance material is set out on page ii of this document.

1    This ACOP, guidance and guide, produced in support of the Pressure Systems Safety Regulations 2000 (SI 2000 No 128), has been the subject of consultation with representatives from employers, trades unions, local authorities, independent experts, government departments and the Health and Safety Commission and other interested parties. It is aimed at dutyholders under the Regulations (users, owners, competent persons, designers, manufacturers, importers, suppliers and installers).

2    Although only the courts can give an authoritative interpretation of law, in considering the application of these Regulations and guidance to people working under another's direction, the following should be considered:

> If people working under the control and direction of others are treated as self-employed for tax and national insurance purposes, they are nevertheless treated as their employees for health and safety purposes. It may therefore be necessary to take appropriate action to protect them. If any doubt exists about who is responsible for the health and safety of a worker, this could be clarified and included in the terms of a contract. However, remember, a legal duty under section 3 of the Health and Safety at Work Act (HSW Act) cannot be passed on by means of a contract and there will still be duties towards others under section 3 of the HSW Act. If such workers are employed on the basis that they are responsible for their own health and safety, legal advice should be sought before doing so.

3    Each section of this Code gives practical guidance on a specific regulation, the number, title and content of which appear at the head of each section.

4    Words and expressions which are defined in the HSW Act[1] or in the Pressure Systems Safety Regulations 2000 (PSSR) have the same meaning in this Code, guidance and guide unless the context requires otherwise. Where the expression 'user/owner' is used in the Code, guidance or guide it should be read as an abbreviated form of 'user of an installed system or owner of a mobile system'.

5    In order to accommodate the implementation of the Pressure Equipment Directive (PED), adopted in May 1997, the Pressure Systems and Transportable Gas Containers Regulations (PSTGCR) (SI 1989 No 2169) have been revoked and replaced with new consolidated regulations, the Pressure Systems Safety Regulations 2000. Transportable gas containers were removed from the scope of PSTGCR by the Carriage of Dangerous Goods (Classification, Packaging and Labelling) and Use of Transportable Pressure Receptacles Regulations 1996 (CDGCPL2) (SI 1996 No 2092). Transportable gas containers are covered by CDGCPL2 as transportable pressure receptacles.

6    The aim of PSSR is to prevent serious injury from the hazard of stored energy as a result of the failure of a pressure system or one of its component parts. The Regulations are concerned with steam at any pressure, gases which exert a pressure in excess of 0.5 bar above atmospheric pressure and fluids which may be mixtures of liquids, gases and vapours where the gas or vapour phase may exert a pressure in excess of 0.5 bar above atmospheric pressure.

7    PSSR is concerned with the risks created by a release of stored energy through system failure. With the exception of the scalding effects of steam, the Regulations do not consider the hazardous properties of the contents released following system failure. The stored contents properties are of concern only to the extent that they may be liable to accelerate wear and cause a more rapid deterioration in the condition of the system, so leading to an increased risk of

failure. The risk from steam includes not only any possible deterioration in the condition of the system, which could increase the risk of failure, but also its scalding effect in the event of release. PSSR does not deal with all the hazards arising from the operation of such a system. The contents may be highly toxic or the plant may form part of a major hazard site. These aspects are all subject to separate legislative requirements and dutyholders will need to consider these other aspects when deciding on the level of precautions required.

8    In the case of some storage systems where gas is kept in liquid form at very low temperatures in a tank, the pressure above the liquid is below 0.5 bar (gauge) and PSSR would not apply unless the pressure rises above 0.5 bar (gauge). The Regulations do not apply simply as a result of pressure exerted by a head of liquid. Moreover, the Regulations do not aim to deal with vacuum conditions.

9    All references to pressures in this Code, guidance and guide relate to pressures above atmospheric pressure. As the term 'bar' is the one most often used and understood in industry, this term is used throughout. However, for convenience a list of equivalent values for 1 bar expressed in other units is given below.

1 bar = 14.5038 psi (pounds per square inch)
$\quad\quad$ 29.530 in of Hg (inches of mercury)
$\quad\quad$ 33.4553 ft of $H_2O$ (feet of water)
$\quad\quad$ 0.986923 atmospheres
$\quad\quad$ $10^5$ N/m$^2$ (Newtons per square metre)
$\quad\quad$ $10^5$ Pa (Pascals)
$\quad\quad$ 1.020 kgf/cm$^2$ (kilogramme force per square centimetre)
$\quad\quad$ 10197.2 kgf/m$^2$ (kilogramme force per square metre)

10    The amount of stored energy in a vessel is generally considered to be directly related to the volume of the vessel and the pressure of the contents. The measure of the stored energy has been expressed by multiplying the pressure by the internal volume (P x V), ie the pressure-volume product. If the values used are bar for pressure and litres for volume, the measure (or product) is given in bar litres.

**Interface between the Pressure Equipment Directive and the implementing regulations in the UK: the Pressure Equipment Regulations 1999 (PER)**

11    The Pressure Equipment Directive arose from the European Community (EC) programme for eliminating technical barriers to trade and is formulated under the 'New Approach'. Its purpose is to harmonise national laws regarding the design, manufacture and conformity assessment of pressure equipment and assemblies subject to an internal pressure greater than 0.5 bar above atmospheric pressure (ie bar gauge). It concerns manufacturers of items such as vessels, pressurised storage containers, heat exchangers, shell and water tube boilers, industrial pipework, safety devices and pressure accessories. It also covers assemblies, ie individual pieces of equipment assembled into a 'package' or 'system'. The Department of Trade and Industry have made the Pressure Equipment Regulations 1999 (SI 1999 No 2001) which implement PED in the United Kingdom.

12    PER therefore covers the supply and putting into service of equipment that would also form whole or part of a pressure system and fall within the scope of PSSR. It must, however, be appreciated that the scope of PER and that of PSSR are not exactly the same. For example, equipment containing steam at or below 0.5 bar gauge does not fall under the scope of PER but does fall within the scope of PSSR.

13    There are also some specific exclusions from PER; many are the same or similar to the exclusions to these Regulations, eg equipment within the scope of other directives, but the full list of exclusions is not exactly the same.

14    PER divides pressure equipment into four major categories on the basis of two fundamental hazards: the degree of danger from failure of the equipment (expressed by the product of the pressure of the fluid and the volume of the equipment or DN value for piping products); and the degree of danger from the release of the fluid contained (based on classifications adopted in the directives on dangerous substances). By contrast, PSSR is primarily concerned with the release of stored energy, with the addition of the hazards associated with the release of steam (regardless of the stored energy hazard).

15    Under PER, pressure equipment above certain pressure/volume (or pressure/DN) thresholds will have to meet requirements for design, manufacture and, according to the category of the equipment, certain conformity assessment and testing procedures are to be followed. Equipment below the thresholds will be required to be manufactured according to 'sound engineering practice'. Equipment supplied in accordance with PER will be excepted from the provisions of manufacture and supply in PSSR (see Schedule 1, Part II, paragraph 1 of these Regulations).

16    PER also contains its own list of definitions, which are not the same as those in PSSR. There are overlaps and areas where certain 'grouping' has occurred. For example, PER gives definitions of 'piping' and 'pressure accessories', eg valves, whereas in PSSR piping and valves come within the definition of 'pipework' (see Table 1).

**Table 1** Comparison of definitions of 'pipework' and 'pipeline' in the Pressure Systems Safety Regulations 2000 (PSSR) with 'pipeline' in the Pipeline Safety Regulations (PSR) and 'piping' in the Pressure Equipment Regulations 1999 (PER)

| Pipework | Pipeline |
|---|---|
| *PSSR definition* | |
| As defined in regulation 2: 'a pipe or system of pipes together with associated valves, pumps, compressors and other pressure containing components and includes a hose or bellows but does not include a pipeline or any protective devices'. | As defined in regulation 2: 'a pipe or system of pipes used for the conveyance of relevant fluid across the boundaries of premises, together with any apparatus for inducing or facilitating the flow of relevant fluid through, or through a part of, the pipe or system, and any valves, valve chambers, pumps, compressors and similar works which are annexed to, or incorporated in the course of, the pipe or system'. |
| *PSR definition (abbreviated)* | |
| No specific definition, but see 'pipeline' definition. | A pipe or system of pipes together with any apparatus and works (eg associated apparatus such as valves, pumps, compressors etc including equipment for: treating the fluid; supplying energy to the apparatus, ie power source; providing information, ie control system; the cathodic protection; and any structure for supporting the pipeline) for the conveyance of any fluid (subject to exclusions). |
| *PER definition* | |
| No specific definition - PER defines 'piping' which means piping components such as lengths of pipe, flanges, elbows, tees etc joined together for the transport of fluids. Piping does not include associated valves, pumps, compressors etc which are classified as 'pressure accessories'. | No specific definition - 'pipeline' is covered by the definition of 'piping', and all pipelines are considered to be pressure equipment (subject to exclusions). As for pipework, the associated valves, compressors, pumps etc are considered as 'pressure accessories'. |

## Citation and commencement

*(1)    These Regulations may be cited as the Pressure Systems Safety Regulations 2000 and shall come into force on 21st February 2000.*

## Interpretation

*(1)    In these Regulations, unless the context otherwise requires -*

*"the 1974 Act" means the Health and Safety at Work etc. Act 1974;*

*"the CDGCPL Regulations" means the Carriage of Dangerous Goods (Classification, Packaging and Labelling) and Use of Transportable Pressure Receptacles Regulations 1996[(a)];*

*"competent person" means a competent individual person (other than an employee) or a competent body of persons corporate or unincoporate; and accordingly any reference in these Regulations to a competent person performing a function includes a reference to his performing it through his employees;*

*"danger" in relation to a pressure system means reasonably foreseeable danger to persons from system failure, but (except in the case of steam) it does not mean danger from the hazardous characteristics of the relevant fluid other than from its pressure;*

*"examination" means a careful and critical scrutiny of a pressure system or part of a pressure system, in or out of service as appropriate, using suitable techniques, including testing where appropriate, to assess -*

*(a)    its actual condition; and*

*(b)    whether, for the period up to the next examination, it will not cause danger when properly used if normal maintenance is carried out, and for this purpose "normal maintenance" means such maintenance as it is reasonable to expect the user (in the case of an installed system) or owner (in the case of a mobile system) to ensure is carried out independently of any advice from the competent person making the examination;*

*"the Executive" means the Health and Safety Executive;*

*"installed system" means a pressure system other than a mobile system;*

*"maximum allowable pressure" and "minimum allowable pressure" mean the maximum pressure and minimum pressure respectively for which a pressure vessel is designed;*

*"mobile system" means a pressure system which can be readily moved between and used in different locations but it does not include a pressure system of a locomotive;*

*"owner" in relation to a pressure system means the employer or self-employed person who owns the pressure system or, if he does not have a place of business in Great Britain, his agent in Great Britain or, if there is no such agent, the user;*

*(a) S.I. 1996/2092.*

"*pipeline*" means a pipe or system of pipes used for the conveyance of relevant fluid across the boundaries of premises, together with any apparatus for inducing or facilitating the flow of relevant fluid through, or through a part of, the pipe or system, and any valves, valve chambers, pumps, compressors and similar works which are annexed to, or incorporated in the course of, the pipe or system;

"*pipework*" means a pipe or system of pipes together with associated valves, pumps, compressors and other pressure containing components and includes a hose or bellows but does not include a pipeline or any protective devices;

"*pressure system*" means -

(a)  a system comprising one or more pressure vessels of rigid construction, any associated pipework and protective devices;

(b)  the pipework with its protective devices to which a transportable pressure receptacle is, or is intended to be, connected; or

(c)  a pipeline and its protective devices,

which contains or is liable to contain a relevant fluid, but does not include a transportable pressure receptacle;

"*protective devices*" means devices designed to protect the pressure system against system failure and devices designed to give warning that system failure might occur, and include bursting discs;

"*relevant fluid*" means -

(a)  steam;

(b)  any fluid or mixture of fluids which is at a pressure greater than 0.5 bar above atmospheric pressure, and which fluid or mixture of fluids is -

(i)  a gas, or

(ii)  a liquid which would have a vapour pressure greater than 0.5 bar above atmospheric pressure when in equilibrium with its vapour at either the actual temperature of the liquid or 17.5 degrees Celsius; or

(c)  a gas dissolved under pressure in a solvent contained in a porous substance at ambient temperature and which could be released from the solvent without the application of heat;

"*safe operating limits*" means the operating limits (incorporating a suitable margin of safety) beyond which system failure is liable to occur;

"*scheme of examination*" means the written scheme referred to in regulation 8;

"*system failure*" means the unintentional release of stored energy (other than from a pressure relief system) from a pressure system;

"*transportable pressure receptacle*" has the same meaning as in regulation 2(1) of the CDGCPL Regulations;

"*user*" in relation to a pressure system, or a vessel to which regulation 15 applies, means the employer or self-employed person who has control of the operation of the pressure system or such a vessel or, in the case of a pressure system or such a vessel at or in -

(a) *a mine within the meaning of section 180 of the Mines and Quarries Act 1954[a] it means the manager for the time being of that mine;*

(b) *a quarry within the meaning of regulation 3 of the Quarries Regulations 1999[b] it means the operator for the time being of that quarry.*

*(2) Any reference in these Regulations to anything being in writing or written (including any reference to anything being kept in writing) shall include reference to its being in a form -*

(a) *in which it is capable of being reproduced as a written copy when required;*

(b) *which is secure from loss or unauthorised interference.*

*(3) In these Regulations, unless the context otherwise requires, any reference to -*

(a) *a numbered regulation or Schedule is a reference to the regulation or Schedule in these Regulations so numbered;*

(b) *a numbered paragraph is a reference to that paragraph so numbered in the regulation or Schedule in which that reference appears.*

(a) *1954 c.70; amended by S.I. 1993/1987.*
(b) *S.I. 1999/2024.*

### Competent person

17    The term 'competent person' refers not to the individual employee who carries out duties under the Regulations but to the body which employs the person charged with those duties. Thus, the definition of competent person makes it clear that the legal duty to comply rests with a competent person's employer, and not with an individual, unless that person is self-employed.

### Danger

18    The Regulations are concerned with reasonably foreseeable danger to people from the unintentional release of stored energy. In addition, they deal with the scalding effects of steam which is classed as a relevant fluid irrespective of pressure. Leaks of gas, for instance, which do not have the potential to cause injury from stored energy, are not covered. Risk of injury from escapes of toxic or flammable materials are covered under other statutory provisions.

### Examination

19    In the context of these Regulations, the term examination relates solely to examinations carried out under the written scheme of examination, ie ones conducted to assess the condition of those parts of the system which may give rise to danger (as defined) in the event of an uncontrolled release of stored energy.

### Installed system and mobile system

20    The Regulations distinguish between those systems which are essentially fixed in a permanent location (installed) and those which are normally and frequently moved from place to place (mobile).

21    For installed systems the user is responsible for compliance with regulations 7 to 12, and 14. In the case of mobile systems the owner is

responsible. If the owner does not have a place of business in Great Britain and has no agent in Great Britain, the user is responsible.

## Pipework

22   This term covers all parts of the system except pressure vessels and protective devices. (See paragraph 51 for specific guidance on the application of the terms pipework and protective devices on gas regulators. See also Table 1, on page 4, for the interface between the terms 'pipework' and 'pipeline' used in these Regulations and the Pressure Equipment Regulations respectively.)

## Pipeline

23   Only pipelines (and their protective devices) for gases and liquefied gases within the definition of relevant fluid are covered as a pressure system. 'Pipeline' also covers the compressors, valves, associated pipework and other apparatus used to cause the gas to flow through the pipeline system. The definition extends to the primary shut-off valve at each end of the pipeline. But see also the exceptions in paragraphs 4 and 5 of Schedule 1, Part I relating to the operation of pipelines. In particular, pipelines and their protective devices where the pressure does not exceed 2 bar (gauge) are excepted from these Regulations. This guidance should be read in conjunction with the publication *A guide to the Pipelines Safety Regulations 1996. Guidance on Regulations.*[2] (See also Table 1, on page 4, for the interface between the definition of the term 'pipeline' used in these Regulations and the Pipelines Safety Regulations.)

## Pressure system

24   The Regulations define three types of system:

(a)   a system comprising a pressure vessel, its associated pipework and protective devices. It is necessary for there to be a pressure vessel in the system for the Regulations to apply under this definition. Where there is more than one system on the premises, whether interconnected or not, the user/owner is responsible for deciding where the boundaries for each system occur;

(b)   pipework with its protective devices to which a transportable pressure receptacle is, or is intended to be, connected. A transportable pressure receptacle on its own is not a pressure system as defined. Pipework containing a relevant fluid (other than steam) at a pressure of 0.5 bar or less is outside the scope of the Regulations;

(c)   a pipeline with its protective devices.

Although there is no definition of pressure vessel in the Regulations, the term is well understood technically. For the purposes of these Regulations, a pressure vessel may be regarded as a vessel used, or intended to be used, to contain a relevant fluid.

## Protective devices

25   'Protective device' includes any protective control or measuring equipment which is essential to prevent a dangerous situation from arising. Instrumentation and control equipment would be classed as a protective device in the following situations:

(a)   where it has to function correctly in order to be able to protect the system; and

(b) where it prevents the safe operating limits being exceeded in situations where no other protective device is provided (for example, where the relevant fluid is so toxic that it cannot be released to atmosphere). In these cases the control equipment is itself the protective device.

Protective devices which protect a system which contains or is liable to contain a relevant fluid are covered by the Regulations even if they are located on a part of the system which does not contain a relevant fluid.

**Relevant fluid**

26    The following conditions have to be fulfilled for a fluid to be a relevant fluid within the scope of the Regulations:

(a)    the pressure has to be greater than 0.5 bar above atmospheric (except for steam). Where the pressure varies with time, then the maximum pressure that is normally reached should be the determining factor;

(b)    either the fluid should be a gas or mixture of gases under the actual conditions in that part of the system or a liquid which would turn into a gas if system failure occurred. Therefore the Regulations will cover compressed air (a mixture of gases) as well as other compressed gases such as nitrogen, acetylene and oxygen. The definition will include also hot water contained above its boiling point at atmospheric pressure (pressurised hot water) or aqueous solutions where a vapour pressure above 0.5 bar (gauge) is generated. Classifications of gases are given in standards in the BS 5045 series which lists gases under separate headings as permanent gases and liquefiable gases.

27    Only those parts of a system which contain a relevant fluid fall within the scope of the Regulations, except protective devices which are within scope irrespective of whether they contain a relevant fluid provided that they form part of a system which contains or is liable to contain a relevant fluid. Except in the case of steam, once the pressure along a line of pipework drops below 0.5 bar (gauge), there is no longer a relevant fluid and that part of the pipework is then no longer part of the system covered by the Regulations.

28    For the definition of relevant fluid not to apply the user/owner should be able to show clear evidence that the system does not contain (and is not liable to contain) a relevant fluid under foreseeable operating conditions. See also paragraph 196 which gives information on Schedule 1, Part I, exception 4(b) dealing with unintentional pressurisation.

29    In some cases a fluid will consist of a mixture of gas and liquid, and in others a liquid with gas dissolved in it. The Regulations are intended to cover the former example but not the latter. To determine whether the fluid is a relevant fluid as defined, it is necessary to establish whether the gaseous element will separate out from the liquid with time to produce a vapour pressure in excess of 0.5 bar (gauge). The definition of relevant fluid thus excludes from scope motor gasoline and stabilised crude oils in which the vapour pressure of a dissolved relevant fluid is suppressed by the lower vapour pressure of other constituents.

30    In the case of some storage systems where gas is kept in liquid form at very low temperatures in a tank, the pressure above the liquid is below 0.5 bar (gauge) and the Regulations would not apply unless the pressure rises above 0.5 bar (gauge).

31   The reference to a gas dissolved under pressure in a solvent contained in a porous substance covers acetylene.

**System failure**

32   Releases of stored energy through properly sized pressure relief equipment are not to be regarded as system failure, as such pressure-relieving arrangements should form part of the normal protection of a properly designed pressure system.

**User**

33   Once a pressure system is installed, the primary duty for compliance rests with the user.

**Requirement for anything in writing or written**

34   These provisions have been added to clarify that any information that is required to be provided in a written form (eg written scheme of examination), or in writing (eg agreement to postpone a due examination), can (subject to the conditions) be provided in any suitable means, for example using computer software.

**Competent persons**

35   The term 'competent person' is used in connection with two distinct functions:

(a)   drawing up or certifying schemes of examination (regulation 8); and

(b)   carrying out examinations under the scheme (regulation 9).

The general guidance at paragraphs 35-41 relates to both functions. Paragraphs 103-119 deal with schemes of examination and paragraphs 130-137 deal with examinations themselves.

36   Although separate guidance is given on these functions, this does not mean that they have to be carried out by different competent persons. In addition, the user/owner may seek advice from a competent person on other matters relating to these Regulations. For example, advice could be sought on the scope of the written scheme (see paragraphs 110 and 111). In such circumstances, a competent person would be acting solely as an adviser, rather than as a competent person as defined.

37   It is the responsibility of the user/owner to select a competent person capable of carrying out the duties in a proper manner with sufficient expertise in the particular type of system. In some cases, the necessary expertise will lie within the user's/owner's own organisation (but see paragraph 40 for guidance on independence). In such cases, the user/owner is acting as competent person and is responsible for compliance with the Regulations. However, small or medium-sized businesses may not have sufficient in-house expertise. If this is the case, they should use a suitably qualified and experienced independent competent person. Whether the competent person is drawn from within the user's/owner's organisation or from outside, they should have sufficient understanding of the systems in question to enable them to draw up schemes of examination or certify them as suitable.

38   A competent person capable of drawing up schemes of examination or examining a simple system may not have the expertise, knowledge and experience to act as competent person for more complex systems. For a number of systems, including the larger or more complex, it is unlikely that one individual will have sufficient knowledge and expertise to act on their own. A competent person should be chosen who has available a team of employees with the necessary breadth of knowledge and experience.

39   In general terms, the competent person should have:

(a)   staff with practical and theoretical knowledge and actual experience of the relevant systems;

(b)   access to specialist services;

(c)   effective support and professional expertise within their organisation; and

(d)   proper standards of professional probity.

40   Where the competent person is a direct employee of the user's/owner's organisation, there should be a suitable degree of independence from the operating functions of the company. In particular, where the staff are provided from an in-house inspection department and carry out functions in addition to their competent person duties, they should be separately accountable under their job descriptions for their activities as competent persons. They should act in an objective and professional manner with no conflict of interests and should give an impartial assessment of the nature and condition of the system.

41   The competent person is responsible for all examinations. For example, where ancillary examination methods (eg non-destructive testing) are undertaken by another person or body, the competent person should accept responsibility for the results of these tests and their interpretation.

42   It is for users to select a competent person to carry out the duties required by these Regulations. The following bodies may provide competent person services:

(a)   a user company;

(b)   a third-party organisation/external company; or

(c)   a self-employed person.

43   Accreditation to BS EN 45004: 1995 *General criteria for operation of the various types of bodies performing inspection* is an indication of the competence of an inspection department, organisation or self-employed person. Accreditation is carried out on behalf of Government by the United Kingdom Accreditation Service (UKAS). Accreditation to BS EN 45004 is recommended for bodies acting as competent persons engaged to draw up or certify a written scheme of examination or conduct examinations for major systems (as detailed in paragraph 105(c)). Users/owners may also wish to consider using accredited bodies for other categories of system. Accreditation to BS EN 45004 is voluntary.

## Examination

44 Although the Regulations apply to all pressure systems as defined, periodic examination is restricted to those parts of the system covered by the written scheme of examination required by regulation 8. The effect of the Regulations is therefore to focus attention on the initial integrity of the whole system when newly installed (regulations 4, 5 and 6) and its maintenance (regulation 12), while limiting subsequent examinations to those parts in which a defect may give rise to danger (regulations 8, 9 and 10).

45 Any suitable inspection technique may be used, including on-line examination, if it is adequate to assess fitness for continued use. There is no requirement to open up equipment for internal examination, provided that the inspection technique is appropriate.

## Installed system and mobile system

46 Some storage tanks for relevant fluids are installed at several sites during their working life. These tanks are normally secured with permanent connections and should be regarded as installed systems. Similarly, a steam boiler fitted with skids may be installed temporarily to maintain steam supply to the site during the replacement of an existing boiler. (Such an installation should not be treated as a mobile system. This equipment will also require proper testing and checks before it is taken into use, even if it is to be replaced with a permanent boiler in due course).

47 On the other hand, a self-contained mobile air compressor set with an air receiver which is towed to construction sites should be regarded as a mobile system. In circumstances where mobile equipment is hired or leased and assembled at a location, for instance direct pressure blasting equipment, the act of assembling the equipment by a contractor does not create a new owner.

48 Steam locomotives, including model steam engines, are classed as installed systems for the purposes of the Regulations. These locomotives are often owned by individual benefactors or preservation trusts without ready access to technical resources. Users should assume responsibility for the examination and maintenance of these locomotives rather than the owners who would otherwise be responsible for compliance.

49 Lorries carrying cargo loaded or discharged under pressure greater than 0.5 bar (gauge) are mobile systems regardless of whether the pressure source is part of the lorry apparatus or external to the lorry.

## Pressure systems

50 The user/owner should decide, after seeking suitable advice if required, whether pressurised equipment for which they are responsible is covered by these Regulations in practice and, if it is not, what other legislation applies.

## Gas regulators

51 In most cases, gas regulators are installed primarily for process control purposes. Regulators installed for this purpose should be regarded as pipework and included in the written scheme where their failure could give rise to danger. A regulator may sometimes be installed with the primary function of protecting the system. Such regulators should be regarded as protective devices and the Regulations would apply accordingly.

## Safe operating limits

52   These are the limits beyond which the system should not be taken. They are not the ultimate limits beyond which system failure will occur. In establishing the limits within which a system should be operated, there may be a need to take account of matters other than pressure energy and the likelihood of system failure. Small steam generators, for example, present a risk from scalding as opposed to stored energy.

## User

53   The role of the user is generally a corporate responsibility. Often the user will be a firm or organisation in control of the operation of the system and therefore in the best position to comply with the Regulations. The user may not be the occupier or owner of the premises or even the employer of the bulk of the employees who work there. For some pressure systems, such as refrigeration plant, where more than one employer or self-employed person has an interest in the running of the system, a number of factors will determine who has responsibility as the user. These factors may include:

(a)   who decides when the plant will be turned on or off;

(b)   who decides who has access to the plant;

(c)   who is responsible for the controls of the plant; and

(d)   who maintains and runs the plant on a day to day basis.

Some of these factors will have more weight than others. For example, an employer who owns a system may pay a contractor to switch the system on and off (among other things), but retain authority to decide when it should be turned on or off. In this situation, the contractor would not be considered to have control of the operation of the system. Consequently, the duties of the user would rest with the employer who owns the system. It is possible for two employers (or self-employed persons) to devise a way in which the pressure system is controlled so that it is clearly the contractor who has full control of the system's operation. In these circumstances, the duties of the user would be for the second party (the contractor) to fulfil. It must be clear to both parties who is responsible as user under the Regulations.

# Application and duties

*(1)   These Regulations shall apply -*

*(a)   in Great Britain; and*

*(b)   outside Great Britain as sections 1 to 59 and 80 to 82 of the 1974 Act apply by virtue of articles 7 and 8(a) of the Health and Safety at Work etc. Act 1974 (Application outside Great Britain) Order 1995[(a)] save in relation to anything to which articles 4 to 6 of that Order apply.*

*(2)   Subject to Schedule 1 (which sets out exceptions to the Regulations), these Regulations shall apply to or in relation to pressure systems which are used or intended to be used at work.*

*(3)   Any requirement or prohibition imposed by these Regulations on an employer in respect of the activities of his employees shall also extend to a self-employed person in respect of his own activities at work.*

*(4)   Any requirement or prohibition imposed by these Regulations on a person -*

*(a)   who designs, manufactures, imports or supplies any pressure system, or any article which is intended to be a component part of any pressure system, shall extend only to such a system or article designed, manufactured, imported or supplied in the course of a trade, business or other undertaking carried on by him (whether for profit or not);*

*(b)   who designs or manufactures such a system or article shall extend only to matters within his control.*

*(5) The provisions of Schedule 2 (which relate to the modification of duties in cases where pressure systems are supplied by way of lease, hire or other arrangements) shall have effect.*

*(a) S.I. 1995/263.*

54    The primary purpose of the Regulations is to secure the safety of people at work. The Regulations therefore apply to pressure systems used, or intended to be used, at work (but see Schedule 1 for exceptions to all or part of the Regulations). The duties imposed relate to activities at work. They also cover the self-employed, for example a self-employed installer of a pressure system, or a self-employed competent person.

55    There are instances, for example in the gases industry, where it is customary for bulk suppliers of gas to lease pressure vessels and associated systems to customers on a long-term contractual basis. Schedule 2 provides for the owner of the system in such cases to be responsible for discharging the legal duties under certain regulations rather than the user. Such arrangements need to be the subject of a written agreement between the owner and user in each case. Schedule 2 contains details of the regulations concerned.

## PART II  GENERAL

# Design and construction

*(1)   Any person who designs, manufactures, imports or supplies any pressure system or any article which is intended to be a component part of any pressure system shall ensure that paragraphs (2) to (5) are complied with.*

*(2)   The pressure system or article, as the case may be, shall be properly designed and properly constructed from suitable material, so as to prevent danger.*

*(3)   The pressure system or article, as the case may be, shall be so designed and constructed that all necessary examinations for preventing danger can be carried out.*

*(4)   Where the pressure system has any means of access to its interior, it shall be so designed and constructed as to ensure, so far as practicable, that access can be gained without danger.*

*(5)  The pressure system shall be provided with such protective devices as may be necessary for preventing danger; and any such device designed to release contents shall do so safely, so far as is practicable.*

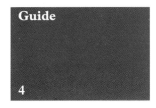

56   This regulation places duties on designers, manufacturers and any person who supplies equipment or a component intended to be part of a pressure system to ensure that it is fit for purpose, so as to prevent danger. Equipment (including assemblies) supplied in accordance with the Pressure Equipment Regulations 1999 is considered to meet these requirements and is, therefore, excepted from this regulation (see Schedule 1, Part II, paragraph 1).

57   Designers and manufacturers should consider at the manufacturing stage both the purpose of the plant and the means of ensuring compliance with these Regulations.

58   The designer, manufacturer, importer or supplier should consider and take due account of the following, where applicable:

(a)   the expected working life (the design life) of the system;

(b)   the properties of the contained fluid;

(c)   all extreme operating conditions including start-up, shutdown and reasonably foreseeable fault or emergency conditions;

(d)   the need for system examination to ensure continued integrity throughout its design life;

(e)   any foreseeable changes to the design conditions;

(f)   conditions for standby operation;

(g)   protection against system failure, using suitable measuring, control and protective devices as appropriate;

(h)   suitable materials for each component part;

(i)   the external forces expected to be exerted on the system including thermal loads and wind loading; and

(j)   safe access for operation, maintenance and examination, including the fitting of access (eg door) safety devices or suitable guards, as appropriate.

Further recommended practice, where appropriate, on these points is given in paragraphs 59 to 75.

**Properties of the fluid**

59   The system should be designed to avoid as far as possible the accumulation of liquids, condensates or sediment in pipework. For example, the design of a compressed air system or of steam pipework should minimise the number of places, such as low points, where liquid can accumulate and should provide for adequate drainage. If necessary, devices should be fitted at appropriate points in the system to allow venting of vapour and/or to prevent a vacuum forming. All pipework drainage should be to a safe place.

60    Special considerations will apply if the pressure vessel is to be used for low temperature storage, eg liquid nitrogen, or a highly corrosive material. It may also be necessary to specify any process materials which should not be put into the system because of incompatibility with the construction materials.

**Extreme operating conditions**

61    Account should be taken of the most onerous combination of temperature, pressure and other relevant parameters to which the equipment may be subjected under reasonably foreseeable circumstances. These should include the conditions which will exist during start-up, shutdown and stand-by operation.

**Examination requirements**

62    Vessels should be provided with suitably sized openings, including manholes and handholes where appropriate, to allow adequate examination of the interior. Where internal examination may be unnecessary or even harmful, for instance because of size or the hazardous nature of the fluid contained within the system, the designer should consider what examinations are needed and provide adequate means for this to be carried out.

**Foreseeable changes**

63    These may include allowances for corrosion if some corrosion is foreseeable and unavoidable, or for wear if stirrers or agitators are liable to cause wear which may give rise to danger. The designer should ensure that the system can safely withstand the consequences of any reasonably foreseeable fault or emergency conditions unless it is to be fitted with appropriate control and protective equipment which will either prevent the conditions arising or enable the stored energy to be safely dissipated.

**Protection against failure**

64    Every plant item in which the pressure can exceed the safe operating limit (ie those which have not been designed to withstand the maximum pressure which can be generated within the system) should be protected, whenever operational, by at least one pressure-relieving or pressure-limiting device. The device should be suitable for its intended duty and should be fitted as close as practicable to the plant item it is designed to protect. Sufficient devices should be fitted at other points to ensure that the pressures inside the system do not exceed the safe operating limits (see paragraph 70 for explanation of accumulation). In the event of a pressure relief device operating, the design should enable the contents to be released in as safe a manner as is practicable.

65    Where part of the system has a lower safe operating limit than other parts, suitable pressure-reducing valves, safety valves, pressure relief and indicating devices should be provided.

66    Some equipment, for example steam receivers, may not necessarily need individual safety valves. However, it should not be possible to isolate them from the device which is providing protection if the source of pressure can still be applied.

67    Suitable measuring or indicating devices should be provided to give clear indications of relevant critical conditions within the system, eg temperatures, pressures, liquid levels. The display of any measuring equipment should be clearly visible. It should be possible to see when safe operating limits are being reached. Suitable moisture filters and/or drains should be provided where moisture would adversely affect the integrity of the system or the operation of any protective device.

68    Equipment, such as boilers, in which a low level (or into which a low flow rate) of water could lead to unsafe conditions should be fitted with at least one suitable water level indicator and to an alarm which sounds when the water level drops to a predetermined value. The indicator should be connected directly to the equipment. Fusible plugs should only be used as the sole low water alarm when other types of low water alarm are not practicable. They should be fitted at the point or points where overheating is first likely to occur if the water level drops. The gauge glasses of tubular water level gauges should be effectively protected to prevent injury from the effects of the glass breaking and the contents being ejected.

69    The pressure-relieving device should be so designed that it will deal adequately, where appropriate, with the dynamic flow characteristics of those fluids which result in two phase flow conditions.

70    The devices and associated inlet and outlet pipework should have an adequate discharge capacity in order to limit pressure to within the safe operating limits. It should reach full discharge capacity within a set limit of overpressure (accumulation). The normal operating pressure of the system should be sufficiently below the setting of the protective device to prevent its premature operation.

**Construction materials**

71    Materials used in construction should be suitable for the intended use. For example, steam boiler stop (crown) valves made from flake graphite (grey) cast iron are not recommended. Account should be taken of the intended duty of the valve, including pressure, temperature, size, frequency of use, nature of contents and any particular foreseeable fault conditions, when selecting valves. The direction of opening and closing should preferably be indicated on valves.

72    Plastic pipes are often used on compressed air systems. However, not all plastics are suitable for use where there is the possibility of their becoming brittle or otherwise damaged due to exposure to heat or other adverse conditions.

**External forces**

73    Account should be taken of any external forces which could affect the integrity of the equipment. These may include the forces exerted on pipework from thermal expansion and contraction, externally applied loads or any reasonably foreseeable vibration or shock loading, for example from water hammer. Suitable expansion bends and/or joints and drains should be incorporated in the pipework as necessary.

**Safe access**

74    Any equipment such as an autoclave to which regular access is required during process operations, eg for loading and unloading, should

be provided with suitable door safety devices. The function of these devices is to securely fasten any door while it is subjected to internal pressure and thereby prevent the risk of the door being violently blown open. The devices should ensure that the vessel cannot be pressurised until the door is securely closed. It should not be possible to open the door until the internal pressure has been fully and suitably vented to atmospheric pressure. The door should be restrained for the first part of its travel until the seal has been broken.

75   Where access is required for the use of tools such as rakes or scrapers and where physical access to the plant item and the area around the door is prevented by an effective guard, this would be a satisfactory alternative way of meeting the pressure interlock requirements.

76   Certain British Standards are in common use for the design and manufacture of some types of pressurised equipment. Where they exist, British Standards, other national or international standards (where they provide an equivalent level of safety) provide a sound basis for the design of pressurised equipment. Although verification of system design and manufacture is not mandatory under these Regulations, it is recommended that independent verification is obtained. This may be specifically required by the manufacturing standards or by some users.

# Provision of information and marking

*(1)   Any person who -*

*(a)   designs for another any pressure system or any article which is intended to be a component part thereof; or*

*(b)   supplies (whether as manufacturer, importer or in any other capacity) any pressure system or any such article,*

*shall provide sufficient written information concerning its design, construction, examination, operation and maintenance as may reasonably foreseeably be needed to enable the provisions of these Regulations to be complied with.*

*(2)   The employer of a person who modifies or repairs any pressure system shall provide sufficient written information concerning the modification or repair as may reasonably foreseeably be needed to enable the provisions of these Regulations to be complied with.*

*(3)   The information referred to in paragraph (1) shall -*

*(a)   in the case of paragraph (1)(a), be provided with the design;*

*(b)   in the case of paragraph (1)(b), be provided with the pressure system or article when it is supplied by that person;*

*(c)   in the case of paragraph (2), be provided to the user of the system immediately after the modification or repair.*

*(4)   Any person who manufactures a pressure vessel shall ensure that before it is supplied by him the information specified in Schedule 3 is marked on the vessel, or on a plate attached to it, in a visible, legible and indelible form; and no person shall import a pressure vessel unless it is so marked.*

*(5) No person shall remove from a pressure vessel any mark or plate containing any of the information specified in Schedule 3.*

*(6) No person shall falsify any mark on a pressure system, or on a plate attached to it, relating to its design, construction, test or operation.*

**Guide**

5

77   The aim of this regulation is to ensure that adequate information about any pressure system subject to the Pressure Systems Safety Regulations 2000 is made available to users/owners by designers, suppliers or those who modify or repair equipment. Basic information about pressure vessels should be permanently marked on the vessel. This information is listed in Schedule 3 of these Regulations.

78   By virtue of the exception at Schedule 1, Part II, paragraph 1, regulations 5(1) and 5(4) apply only to pressure systems which are not supplied in accordance with the Pressure Equipment Regulations 1999.

79   Regulation 5(4) does not apply to a pressure system containing a relevant fluid other than steam where the product of the pressure in bars and internal volume of the vessel, or in systems with more than one vessel each vessel, is less than 250 bar litres (see Schedule 1, Part II, paragraph 2).

**ACOP**

80   The designer or supplier of a pressure system or component part covered by this regulation should consider the most effective way of providing the appropriate information to those who need it.

81   Additional information about pressure vessels and information relevant to the whole system (apart from that already marked on the vessel under regulation 5(4)) should be provided in writing. The purpose being to provide users/owners with sufficient information on the design, construction, examination, operation and maintenance of the equipment to enable them to comply with the requirements of these Regulations. The designer or supplier should use their judgement, knowledge and experience to decide what information is required. Although it is not possible to give a complete list of all the information which might be needed the following items should be considered where relevant:

(a)   design standards used and evidence of compliance with national/European/international standards or documentation showing conformity;

(b)   design pressures (maximum and minimum);

(c)   fatigue life;

(d)   design temperatures (maximum and minimum);

(e)   creep life;

(f)   intended contents, especially where the design has been carried out for a specific process;

(g)   flow rates and discharge capacities;

(h)   corrosion allowances;

(i)   wall thickness;

(j)   volume capacities, especially for storage vessels. Depending on the intended contents these may be expressed as maximum volume, pressure or filling ratio; and

(k)   materials of construction.

82   There may be several stages in the supply chain before the equipment reaches the user/owner. For example, components such as safety devices fabricated by others may be used by a manufacturer or installer of a complete vessel or system. It is important that all relevant information is passed on at each stage of the production or supply process. However, the manufacturer does not have to provide a statement of the safe operating limits if sufficient information is provided to enable the safe operating limits to be determined.

83   Where pressure systems are supplied in accordance with the Pressure Equipment Regulations 1999, it is desirable for the user/owner to satisfy themselves that they have been supplied with appropriate documentation confirming evidence of conformity with EC Directives issued by the manufacturer and, where appropriate, the conformity assessment body.

84   It may be advantageous to the user/owner if the manufacturer of a standard vessel produced in series, such as a steam boiler or air receiver, initially provides the written scheme of examination required by regulation 8. The manufacturer will know how the item was designed to operate and the intended frequency of examinations. However, the competent person will still have to certify the written scheme of examination and fulfil their duties under regulations 8 and 9. For instance, this will include reviewing the written scheme and considering the frequency of examinations according to the rate of deterioration and wear experienced by the system in use.

# Installation

*The employer of a person who installs a pressure system at work shall ensure that nothing about the way in which it is installed gives rise to danger or otherwise impairs the operation of any protective device or inspection facility.*

85   If the installer of the system is also the designer, manufacturer or supplier they will have responsibilities under regulations 4 and 5 as well.

86   When planning the installation, the employer of the installer should ensure that all of the following items which are relevant to the system are actioned (this list is not exhaustive and additional actions may be needed depending on the type of system, its location, and planned operating conditions):

(a)   ensure that those doing the installation have the required training, skills and experience;

(b)   provide adequate supervision, taking into account the complexity of the system being installed;

(c)   prepare suitable foundations to support the system, taking into account the nature of the ground and design loads such as the weight of the system and any likely external forces;

(d)   decide on the most suitable method of lifting and handling the vessel(s), protective devices and pipework so as to avoid accidental damage;

(e)    check for signs of damage in transit;

(f)    protect the system from adverse weather conditions before and during installation;

(g)    remove any protective packaging carefully before commissioning;

(h)    ensure that any hot work such as welding or cutting will not affect the integrity of the system;

(i)    ensure that protective devices are clear of obstruction, operate correctly without hindrance or blockage and that the discharge is routed to a safe place;

(j)    ensure that any access doors/hatches are clear of obstruction and operate correctly;

(k)    ensure that any labels or markings attached to the system are clearly visible;

(l)    provide adequate access for maintenance and examination purposes;

(m)    provide suitable physical protection against mechanical damage, eg accidental impact by vehicles;

(n)    allow sufficient space for access around and beneath valves, in particular drain valves;

(o)    clear away any debris such as metal shavings or dust arising from the installation process; and

(p)    have the installation work checked and approved on completion by a suitably qualified person.

**Compressed air systems**

87    Additional points which should be noted for compressed air systems are:

(a)    the installation site should provide a well-ventilated, cool and clean air environment;

(b)    intercoolers and aftercoolers should, where they are cooled by air, be located so that the air flow over their surfaces is not obstructed;

(c)    inlet air should be drawn from an area which is free from potentially flammable or corrosive concentrations of fumes or vapours; and

(d)    the inlet air should not be excessively laden with moisture or dust.

88    The complexity of the planning and installation process will depend on the nature of each individual system and the amount of detail given in the specification for the work. The specification will normally be supplied by the user/owner. It will include any information available from the manufacturer/supplier. There may be a detailed installation specification or a simple broad outline. Whatever the level of information provided, it is the responsibility of the employer of the installer to ensure that nothing in the installation process affects the integrity of the system or could give rise to danger. Nor should it affect the operation of the protective devices or hinder access for maintenance, examination or inspection tasks.

# Safe operating limits

*(1)   The user of an installed system and owner of a mobile system shall not operate the system or allow it to be operated unless he has established the safe operating limits of that system.*

*(2)   The owner of a mobile system shall, if he is not also the user of it -*

*(a)   supply the user with a written statement specifying the safe operating limits of that system established pursuant to paragraph (1); or*

*(b)   ensure that the system is legibly and durably marked with such safe operating limits and that the mark is clearly visible.*

89   This regulation complements regulation 5 which makes the designer, manufacturer and supplier responsible for providing adequate information about the system or its component parts. It prohibits the user/owner from operating the system or allowing it to be operated before the safe operating limits have been established.

**Establishing the limits**

90   Where the system consists of a standard production item, the designer/manufacturer should assess the safe operating limits and pass the relevant information to the user/owner. In these circumstances, the user/owner will not always need to carry out the detailed work required to establish the safe operating limits of the system. In cases where the user/owner has specified the design, the responsibility for establishing the safe operating limits rests with the user/owner.

91   If the user/owner does not have sufficient technical expertise to establish the safe operating limits, an organisation which is competent to carry out the task should be used.

92   The exact nature and type of safe operating limits which need to be specified will depend on the complexity and operating conditions of the particular system. Small, simple systems may need little more than the establishment of the maximum pressure for safe operation. Complex, larger systems are likely to need a wide range of conditions specified, eg maximum and minimum temperatures and pressures, nature, volumes and flow rates of contents, operating times, heat input or coolant flow. In all cases the safe operating limits should incorporate a suitable margin of safety.

**Record keeping**

93   A suitable system for recording and retaining information about safe operating limits and any changes to them should be used. Where the limits have been specified by the designer or manufacturer, then the operating manual supplied with the system should be used to pass on the information. Larger or more complex systems may have the information recorded in several documents. Whatever method is used, the information should be readily available to those people who need it, including the competent person responsible for the examinations in accordance with the written scheme. It is recommended that the details of the safe operating limits are made available to the person operating the system (under the provision of instructions at regulation 11) and retained with the documents required to be kept under regulation 14.

94    For mobile systems the owner must provide the user with a written statement detailing the safe operating limits or ensure that this information is clearly marked on the equipment. Where the system is likely to be on hire for long periods, both a written statement and durable marking are preferable. This should ensure that information about the safe operating limits is always readily available.

**Second-hand systems**

95    Second-hand equipment should be thoroughly assessed so that users/owners are satisfied that the safe operating limits have been established correctly. Often the original design information is not available and, even when it is, the equipment may have deteriorated to an extent where the current safe operating limits are below the original design values.

**Review**

96    Users/owners should ensure that the safe operating limits specified for a system are kept up to date. They should be reviewed at the time of examinations under the written scheme, when significant repairs or modifications are carried out or where there are major changes to the operating conditions, eg a change in the relevant fluid contained within the system. If the safe operating limits are altered, the discharge capacity of the pressure-relieving devices should be reviewed to ensure that the system is adequately protected against overpressure at all times.

97    In order to operate the pressurised plant in a safe manner, the user needs to be aware of its safe operating limits and make sure that these limits are not exceeded.

98    The manufacturer's literature will normally specify the safe operating limits for standard items. However, the manufacturer is not required to specify the safe operating limits as long as sufficient information is provided to allow them to be determined. This is particularly relevant where the manufacturer is not supplying the whole system.

99    The terminology used for different types of systems will vary. For example, the safe operating limit for a boiler may be known as the 'maximum permissible working pressure' whereas for an air receiver it may be described as the 'safe working pressure'. The safe operating limits for refrigeration plant will be expressed in terms of minimum and maximum temperatures. In cases of doubt, or where the information is not clear, further advice should be sought from the manufacturer or other competent organisation.

100   It is preferable for the safe operating limits for mobile systems on hire for short periods to be marked on the equipment itself.

# Written scheme of examination

*(1)    The user of an installed system and owner of a mobile system shall not operate the system or allow it to be operated unless he has a written scheme for the periodic examination, by a competent person, of the following parts of the system, that is to say -*

*(a)    all protective devices;*

23

*(b)    every pressure vessel and every pipeline in which (in either case) a defect may give rise to danger; and*

*(c)    those parts of the pipework in which a defect may give rise to danger,*

*and such parts of the system shall be identified in the scheme.*

*(2)    The said user or owner shall -*

*(a)    ensure that the scheme has been drawn up, or certified as being suitable, by a competent person;*

*(b)    ensure that -*

*(i)    the content of the scheme is reviewed at appropriate intervals by a competent person for the purpose of determining whether it is suitable in current conditions of use of the system; and*

*(ii)    the content of the scheme is modified in accordance with any recommendations made by that competent person arising out of that review.*

*(3)    No person shall draw up or certify a scheme of examination under paragraph (2)(a) unless the scheme is suitable and -*

*(a)    specifies the nature and frequency of examination;*

*(b)    specifies any measures necessary to prepare the pressure system for safe examination other than those it would be reasonable to expect the user (in the case of an installed system) or owner (in the case of a mobile system) to take without specialist advice; and*

*(c)    where appropriate, provides for an examination to be carried out before the pressure system is used for the first time.*

*(4)    References in paragraphs (2) and (3) to the suitability of the scheme are references to its suitability for the purposes of preventing danger from those parts of the pressure system included in the scheme.*

101   Responsibility under this regulation may be summarised as follows:

(a)    the user/owner ensures the scope of the scheme is appropriate, ie which parts of the system are covered (with advice, if necessary, from a suitably experienced adviser); and

(b)    the competent person specifies the nature and frequency of examinations and any special measures needed to prepare the system for safe examination.

Where the written scheme of examination is written by someone other than a competent person, it must be certified as suitable by a competent person.

102   The term 'pipework' has been broadly defined (see paragraph 22). The effect of regulation 8 is to enable the exclusion of most 'pipework' from the written scheme where appropriate. It should be noted, however, that all pipework, irrespective of diameter or pressure, will be subject to the initial integrity, installation, operation and maintenance provisions.

103 Before a pressure system is operated the user/owner must ensure that a written scheme of examination has been prepared. The written scheme of examination should be drawn up by a competent person, or if drawn up by someone other than a competent person, certified as suitable by a competent person. See paragraphs 35 to 41 for general guidance on the role of the competent person and paragraphs 107 to 119 for guidance on the function of the competent person in relation to the written scheme of examination.

**Attributes and role of competent persons**

104 The level of expertise needed by the competent person depends on the size and complexity of the system in question. To illustrate the level of expertise, knowledge and experience needed in different circumstances, pressure systems are divided into three categories as described in paragraph 105. However, in practice there are no clear dividing lines. The three categories should be taken as an indication of the range of systems covered rather than providing clear cut divisions. Each system should be individually assessed and an informed decision made on which of the categories is the most appropriate.

105 The three categories are as follows:

(a) Minor systems include those containing steam, pressurised hot water, compressed air, inert gases or fluorocarbon refrigerants which are small and present few engineering problems. The pressure (above atmospheric pressure) should be less than 20 bar (2.0 MPa) (except for systems with a direct-fired heat source when it should be less than 2 bar (200 kPa)). The pressure-volume product for the largest vessel should be less than $2 \times 10^5$ bar litres (20 MPa m$^3$). The temperatures in the system should be between -20°C and 250°C except in the case of smaller refrigeration systems operating at lower temperatures which will also fall into this category. Pipelines are not included.

(b) Intermediate systems include the majority of storage systems and process systems which do not fall into either of the other two categories. Pipelines are included unless they fall into the major system category.

(c) Major systems are those which because of their size, complexity or hazardous contents require the highest level of expertise in determining their condition. They include steam-generating systems where the individual capacities of the steam-generators are more than 10 MW, any pressure storage system where the pressure-volume product for the largest pressure vessel is more than $10^6$ bar litres (100 MPa m$^3$) and any manufacturing or chemical reaction system where the pressure-volume product for the largest pressure vessel is more than $10^5$ bar litres (10 MPa m$^3$). Pipelines are included if the pressure-volume product is greater than $10^5$ bar litres.

106 The attributes needed for competent persons who draw up or certify schemes of examination relating to minor, intermediate and major systems are shown overleaf.

(a) **Minor systems**

*Staff*

At least one member of staff qualified to incorporated engineer level with adequate relevant experience and knowledge of the law, codes of practice, examination and inspection techniques and understanding of the effects of operation for the system concerned.

*Specialist services*

Established access to basic design and plant operation advice, materials engineering and non-destructive testing (NDT) facilities.

*Organisation*

Sufficient organisation to ensure a reasonable document storage and retrieval system with ready access to relevant law, technical standards and codes.

(b) **Intermediate systems**

*Staff*

Depending on the complexity of the system, at least one senior member of staff of chartered engineer or equivalent status in each relevant discipline and supported by technically qualified and experienced staff with knowledge of the law, codes of practice, examination and inspection techniques and understanding of the effects of operation for the system concerned.

*Specialist services*

In-house or clearly established access to materials engineering, NDT, design and plant operating advice.

*Organisation*

Clear supervisory arrangements with an adequate degree of formal organisation. Appropriate document storage and retrieval system with ready access to relevant law, technical codes and standards.

(c) **Major systems**

*Staff*

Depending on the complexity of the system, at least one senior member of staff of chartered engineer or equivalent status in each relevant discipline and supported by technically qualified and experienced staff with knowledge of the law, codes of practice, examination and inspection techniques and understanding of the effects of operation for the system concerned.

*Specialist services*

In-house or clearly established access to the full range of relevant specialist services in the fields of materials engineering, NDT, design and plant operation.

*Organisation*

Formal structure and clear lines of authority and responsibility set out in a written statement. Formal recruitment and training policies for staff. Effective document storage and retrieval system with ready access to relevant law, technical codes and standards.

**Drawing up the written scheme of examination**

107　The written scheme of examination can be written and certified as suitable either by an independent competent person or by the in-house competent person. For either function, the criteria for competent persons at paragraph 106 should be met, depending on the category of the system.

108　Where the appropriate technical expertise exists in-house, the written scheme may be drawn up by the user of the system and certified as suitable by a competent individual within their own organisation provided they fulfil the requirements for a competent person. Alternatively, there may be sufficient in-house expertise to draw up the scheme but not certify it, in which case the user should employ an independent competent person to carry out the certification.

109　The competent person should ensure that the written scheme specifies:

(a)　which parts of the pressure system need to be subject to examination, ie the scope as defined by the user/owner (see paragraphs 110 and 111); and

(b)　what types of examination are necessary and the intervals between them, ie the content (see paragraphs 112 and 113).

**Scope**

110　The responsibility for ensuring the scope of the written scheme of examination is suitable rests with the user/owner. The user/owner should first establish which parts of the pressure system are pressure vessels, protective devices, or pipework as defined in the Regulations, and then decide which parts of the system should be included in the written scheme. The following guidelines should be used:

(a)　in general, pressure vessels should be included (it might be reasonable to exclude small vessels with low stored energy which form part of a larger system);

(b)　all protective devices should be included, even if they are on a part of the system which is not included;

(c)　pipework, which is widely defined to include pipes, associated valves, pumps, compressors, hoses, bellows and other pressure-containing components, will only need to be included in the scheme if:

(i)　its mechanical integrity is liable to be significantly reduced by corrosion, erosion, fatigue or any other factors; and

(ii)　failure resulting in the sudden release of stored energy would give rise to danger.

111   The user/owner should be able to justify any decision to exclude parts of the system from the scope of the written scheme. To arrive at a properly informed decision, and particularly where parts of the system are to be excluded from the written scheme, users or owners should seek advice from a person with the appropriate and relevant technical expertise and experience. Such a person need not be a competent person as defined in these Regulations. But the person advising on the scope of the written scheme must have an appropriate level of expertise and experience of the particular type of system. The user/owner may choose to seek advice on this matter from a competent person.

**Content**

112   At least the following information should be included in the written scheme of examination:

(a)    those parts of the system which are to be examined;

(b)    identification of the item of plant or equipment;

(c)    the nature of the examination required, including the inspection and testing to be carried out on any protective devices;

(d)    the preparatory work necessary to enable the item to be examined safely;

(e)    specify what examination is necessary before the system is first used, where appropriate;

(f)    the maximum interval between examinations;

(g)    the critical parts of the system which, if modified or repaired, should be examined by a competent person before it is used again;

(h)    the name of the competent person certifying the written scheme; and

(i)    the date of the certification.

113   The nature of the examination should be specified in the written scheme. This may vary from out-of-service examination with the system stripped down, to in-service examination with the system running under normal operating conditions. Some systems (for example fired equipment) may need to undergo both out-of-service and in-service examinations. The competent person may need to seek advice from the manufacturer/supplier on appropriate methods of testing, particularly where internal examination is difficult.

**First examination**

114   Where appropriate, the requirement for an examination before the system is first taken into use should be specified in the written scheme of examination. For equipment supplied in accordance with the Pressure Equipment Regulations 1999, the person who draws up or certifies the written scheme should consider whether an initial examination is appropriate and the form that any such examination should take. This consideration should take account of the results of the conformity assessment to which the equipment was subject before it was placed on

8

28

the market. In general, further assessment of the equipment under the written scheme should be judged on the merits of each individual case.

**Periodicity**

115 When deciding on the periodicity between examinations, the aim should be to ensure that sufficient examinations are carried out to identify at an early stage any deterioration or malfunction which is likely to affect the safe operation of the system. Different parts of the system may be examined at different intervals, depending on the degree of risk associated with each part.

116 Protective devices should be examined at least at the same time and frequency as the plant to which they are fitted. Some protective devices may need to be examined at more frequent intervals. The examination should include checks that the devices function correctly and are properly calibrated or, alternatively, that they have been replaced by recently tested units.

117 All relevant factors should be taken into account when deciding on the appropriate interval between examinations, including:

(a)   the safety record and previous history of the system;

(b)   any generic information available about the particular type of system;

(c)   its current condition, eg due to corrosion/erosion etc (internal and external);

(d)   the expected operating conditions (especially any particularly arduous conditions);

(e)   the quality of fluids used in the system;

(f)   the standard of technical supervision, operation, maintenance and inspection in the user's/owner's organisation; and

(g)   the applicability of any on-stream monitoring.

**Repair/modification**

118 The scheme should, where necessary, specify the type of repair or modification which need to be examined by the competent person carrying out examinations under regulation 9 before the system is put back into use. Alternatively, the user/owner may decide to draw up a comprehensive written method to be followed for certain specified repairs or modifications to all or some of the systems.

**Storage**

119 The written scheme of examination may be kept in hard copy form, stored electronically or on computer disc. If a computer system is used it must be able to reproduce the scheme readily as a written copy, be authenticated by the competent person and be protected from unauthorised alteration.

8

120 The user/owner should decide, in consultation with a person competent to advise as appropriate, whether a written scheme of examination is required. Each system should be considered individually, taking into account the exceptions to all or certain regulations detailed in Schedule 1. The examples given below are for general guidance purposes only and the lists are not exhaustive. The following types of pressurised systems are likely to require a written scheme of examination:

(a)    steam sterilising autoclave and associated pipework and protective devices;

(b)    steam boiler and associated pipework and protective devices;

(c)    pressure cooker;

(d)    gas-loaded hydraulic accumulator, if forming part of a pressure system;

(e)    portable hot water/steam-cleaning unit fitted with a pressure vessel;

(f)    vapour compression refrigeration system where the installed power exceeds 25 kW;

(g)    standard or narrow gauge steam locomotive;

(h)    the components of self-contained breathing apparatus sets (excluding the transportable pressure receptacle); and

(i)    fixed LPG storage system supplying fuel for heating in a workplace.

The following pressurised systems are unlikely to require a written scheme of examination:

(a)    an office hot water urn (for tea making);

(b)    a machine tool hydraulic system;

(c)    portable oxy-fuel gas welding sets; and

(d)    an atmospheric oil storage tank.

121 In practice, it should only be necessary in the case of unusual or complicated systems to set out any special safety precautions which are required to prepare the system for examination. These would only need to be spelt out where the user or owner does not have specialist advice available on these matters.

122 There are many factors to be considered by the competent person when deciding the maximum interval between examinations under the written scheme of examination (see paragraph 117). There can be no hard and fast rules - the competent person should use their judgement and experience to determine the appropriate interval based on the relevant information. However, earlier legislation set out maximum examination intervals for some types of equipment. The competent person may wish to consider using these as a guide when drawing up or certifying the written scheme of examination, if appropriate for that system. For steam plant the period was usually 14 months with more frequent examinations specified where operating conditions were arduous. The examination period for steam receivers linked to such plant was

generally in the range of 26-38 months. Air receivers on compressed air systems were generally examined every 24-48 months, with examinations taking place less frequently, ie every 72 months where corrosion was minimal and maintenance of safety standards was high.

**Review**

123   The written scheme must be 'suitable' in all the circumstances so it follows that it will be necessary to review it from time to time. It is the user's/owner's responsibility under the Regulations to ensure that the content of the written scheme is reviewed periodically by a competent person.

124   While a review may be carried out at any time, it is good practice to do this when an examination has been completed and before the written report of that examination is issued. The competent person may decide that the period between each examination should be altered and it will, therefore, be necessary to revise the written scheme. For example, as the age of some plant increases, more frequent examinations may be needed or their content or type may have to be changed.

125   A review which alters the frequency of examinations under the written scheme cannot be used to extend the date by which the next examination is due to take place as specified in the last written report. Under regulation 9(5)(c), the competent person will have specified in the last written report the date by which the next examination should take place and after which the system cannot be operated without a further examination. That requirement must be met unless a postponement is made in accordance with regulation 9(7).

# Examination in accordance with the written scheme

*(1)   Subject to paragraph (7), the user of an installed system and the owner of a mobile system shall -*

*(a)   ensure that those parts of the pressure system included in the scheme of examination are examined by a competent person within the intervals specified in the scheme and, where the scheme so provides, before the system is used for the first time; and*

*(b)   before each examination take all appropriate safety measures to prepare the system for examination, including any such measures as are specified in the scheme of examination pursuant to regulation 8(3)(b).*

*(2)   Where a competent person undertakes an examination for the purposes of paragraph (1) he shall carry out that examination properly and in accordance with the scheme of examination.*

*(3)   Where a competent person has carried out an examination for the purposes of paragraph (1) he shall, subject to paragraph (4) and regulation 14(4),\* make a written report of the examination, sign it or add his name to it, date it and send it to the user (in the case of an installed system) or owner (in the case of a mobile system); and the said report shall be so sent as soon as is practicable after completing the examination (or, in the case of integrated installed systems where the examination is part of a series, as soon as is practicable after completing the last examination in that series), and in any event to arrive -*

\* There is an error in the Statutory Instrument – it should not refer to regulation 14(4), as it does not exist.

(a)   within 28 days of the completion of the examination (or, in the case of integrated installed systems where the examination is part of a series, within 28 days of the completion of the last examination in that series); or

(b)   before the date specified in the report under paragraph (5)(b),

whichever is sooner.

(4)   Where the competent person referred to in paragraph (3) is the user (in the case of an installed system) or owner (in the case of a mobile system) the requirement in that paragraph to send the report to the user or owner shall not apply, but he shall make the report by the time it would have been required to have been sent to him under that paragraph if he had not been the competent person.

(5)   The report required by paragraph (3) shall -

(a)   state which parts of the pressure system have been examined, the condition of those parts and the results of the examination;

(b)   specify any repairs or modifications to, or changes in the established safe operating limits of, the parts examined which, in the opinion of the competent person, are necessary to prevent danger or to ensure the continued effective working of the protective devices, and specify the date by which any such repairs or modifications must be completed or any such changes to the safe operating limits must be made;

(c)   specify the date within the limits set by the scheme of examination after which the pressure system may not be operated without a further examination under the scheme of examination; and

(d)   state whether in the opinion of the competent person the scheme of examination is suitable (for the purpose of preventing danger from those parts of the pressure system included in it) or should be modified, and if the latter state the reasons.

(6)   The user of an installed system and the owner of a mobile system which has been examined under this regulation shall ensure that the system is not operated, and no person shall supply such a mobile system for operation, after (in each case) -

(a)   the date specified under paragraph (5)(b), unless the repairs or modifications specified under that paragraph have been completed, and the changes in the established safe operating limits so specified have been made; or

(b)   the date specified under paragraph (5)(c) (or, if that date has been postponed under paragraph (7), the postponed date) unless a further examination has been carried out under the scheme of examination.

(7)   The date specified in a report under paragraph (5)(c) may be postponed to a later date by agreement in writing between the competent person who made the report and the user (in the case of an installed system) or owner (in the case of a mobile system) if -

(a)   such postponement does not give rise to danger;

(b)   only one such postponement is made for any one examination; and

(c)   such postponement is notified by the user or owner in writing to the enforcing authority for the premises at which the pressure system is situated, before the date specified in the report under paragraph (5)(c).

*(8) Where the competent person referred to in paragraph (7) is the user (in the case of an installed system) or owner (in the case of a mobile system) the reference in that paragraph to an agreement in writing shall not apply, but there shall be included in the notification under sub-paragraph (c) of that paragraph a declaration that the postponement will not give rise to danger.*

*(9) The owner of a mobile system shall ensure that the date specified under paragraph (5)(c) is legibly and durably marked on the mobile system and that the mark is clearly visible.*

**Guide**

126 Although this regulation places duties on the competent person in relation to carrying out the examination, there is a clear duty on users/owners to ensure that the equipment is not operated beyond the date specified in the current examination report.

127 The words 'as soon as is practicable' in regulation 9(3) are intended to ensure that where repairs have to be carried out within a short timescale, there is no delay between the time the examination is actually carried out and the receipt by the user of the examination report. However, where examinations are concentrated into a short period of time for reasons of efficiency, for instance on large integrated chemical plants, it may be unreasonable to expect all the reports to be completed at the same time. In these circumstances, the competent person should complete the reports and forward them within 28 days of the completion of the final examination in that series.

128 In regulation 9(5)(c) the date referred to is the date beyond which the competent person has decided the system should not be operated for safety reasons, based upon the results of the examination under the written scheme. In any case, the date set for the next examination must not exceed the period stated in the written scheme. For example, if examinations are at two-yearly intervals, the next examination will be due by a date two years after the last examination.

129 Regulation 9(7) makes provision for the postponement of the next examination subject to the fulfilment of certain conditions. It is for the user/owner to fulfil all these conditions before the examination can legally be postponed. Details of the postponement have to be notified by the user/owner to the enforcing authority (ie the Health and Safety Executive or the Environmental Health Department of the Local Authority).

**9**

**ACOP**

130 The user/owner should ensure that any necessary preparatory work is completed so that the competent person can carry out the examination safely. Preparatory works may be specified to a greater or lesser extent in the written scheme. Whether any special preparatory works form part of the written scheme or not, the user/owner should consider the type of preparations required, seeking advice from a suitably qualified person where necessary. According to the type of system, the preparatory works may need to include:

(a)     cooling the system;

(b)     positively isolating the parts of the system to be examined;

(c)     returning the system to ambient conditions;

(d)     removing the contents;

(e)     venting vessels;

(f)     erecting suitable staging for access;

(g)   removing protective devices;

(h)   ensuring that, where appropriate, vessels, pipework etc are visible and accessible (ie by removing brickwork or lagging);

(i)   cleaning surfaces;

(j)   removing scale and other deposits;

(k)   removing pieces of insulation;

(l)   ensuring that any ancillary testing equipment is available; and

(m)   arranging for the system to be tested (for example for leaks) where appropriate.

131   The competent person should have sufficient practical and theoretical knowledge and actual experience of the type of system under examination to enable defects or weaknesses to be identified and an assessment made of their significance in terms of the integrity and safety of the equipment.

132   The competent person should examine and report on all parts of the system covered by the written scheme of examination. The competent person should be satisfied that, as a result of the examination, the condition of the parts included in the written scheme and their fitness for continued use has been properly assessed. The following points (although not exhaustive) should aid the competent person's decisions:

(a)   the age and known history of the part or system;

(b)   the nature of the relevant fluid;

(c)   the conditions of use;

(d)   the length of time since the last examination; and

(e)   the expected operating conditions and maintenance regime until the date of the next examination.

133   Unless the user or owner informs the competent person of an intended change of use, the assessment of the system's fitness should be based on the current operating conditions and method of use continuing unchanged. The competent person should assume that normal maintenance will be carried out as defined in regulation 2 under 'examination'.

134   The report should be based on the actual condition of the system as found during the examination. If repairs are carried out as a result of the examination, the report should include details of the fault and the remedial action taken even if the repair works are finished before the examination has been completed.

135   The competent person should consider whether any changes are needed in the safe operating limits, or in the scheme of examination. The report may state that continued use of the system is dependent on altering certain specified operating conditions or undertaking specific maintenance tasks.

136  The competent person may decide that the risk of danger may be significantly increased if the next examination is delayed until a date set in accordance with the current written scheme. In these circumstances, the written scheme should be reviewed and an earlier date set beyond which the system should not be operated without a further examination.

137  At the end of the examination, the competent person should be satisfied that the protective devices, especially any safety valves, have been tested and set correctly. Where protective devices which have been removed during an examination are found to be defective, the cause of the problem should be investigated further by the user/owner and the necessary corrective measures taken (see also paragraphs 145-150 for guidance on action in case of imminent danger).

138  Although the user/owner is not directly responsible for the quality of the examination (and in many cases will not be able to judge the quality of the work undertaken by the competent person), they will need to be assured that the examination has been carried out in a satisfactory manner.

139  The user's/owner's co-operation will be needed to ensure that the system is properly prepared and made available in time for the competent person to carry out the examination.

140  Adequate advance notice should be given to the competent person that an examination is due and the user/owner should make the system available in good time.

141  All parts of the system covered by the scheme must be examined within the intervals specified in the written scheme of examination. Where there are several identical vessels on-site operated by the same user, a form of staged examination may be used. To illustrate the principle of staged examination consider the following hypothetical example:

> A written scheme covers four identical vessels and specifies a frequency of examination of five years. It is acceptable to examine a different vessel each year within the group of four provided they are all examined within the five-year period. Where such a staged examination scheme is used, the competent person should be satisfied that this approach is appropriate as the basis of the written scheme. It is not acceptable to examine one vessel after five years, another five years later and so on since not all of the vessels will be examined within the five-year period specified for each vessel. Nor is it permissible under these Regulations to carry out an examination of a sample of the vessels as representative of the population.

142  The user/owner and competent person should remember that there are other hazards not covered by these Regulations which may need to be considered prior to an examination (for example means of access, entry into confined spaces, lack of oxygen, hazards of toxic substances, asbestos in lagging). The risks posed by these hazards need to be assessed to comply with the requirements of the Management of Health and Safety at Work Regulations 1999[3] and other more specific provisions, and the appropriate precautions required should be taken. The person who carries out an examination, either individually or as part of a team, will need to take reasonable care and to co-operate fully with other workers and with the user/owner to comply with the general duties of employees at work placed on them by section 7 of the HSW Act.

**Mobile systems**

143 For mobile systems the date of the next examination has to be marked on the system. A permanent form of marking, such as engraving, is not required. It will generally be sufficient if the date is painted on the equipment. For a vehicle it may be most convenient to put the marking in the cab. The owner of a mobile system may need to make a greater effort than the user of an installed system to ensure that examinations are carried out, particularly in the case of plant on long-term hire. A contractual agreement may be needed between the owner and the user to ensure that the competent person has access to the equipment at the appropriate time.

**Format of reports**

144 No particular format is laid down for the report as systems vary in size and complexity. The format can be chosen to fit in with the record keeping systems of the user/owner and competent person. Computer-generated reports with appropriate validation are acceptable and this is likely to speed up the despatch of reports from centrally organised inspection organisations with locally based inspectors. Any secure system that can be validated as the sole record keeping medium is acceptable. Suggested items for inclusion in the report include the following:

(a)   name and address of owner;

(b)   address, location of system and name of user (if different from owner);

(c)   whether subject to a written agreement under Schedule 2;

(d)   identification of system or parts examined;

(e)   condition of system or parts examined;

(f)   parts not examined;

(g)   result of the examination;

(h)   any repairs needed and the time scale for completion;

(i)   any changes in the safe operating limits and the date by which they should be made;

(j)   any change in the written scheme of examination;

(k)   date by which the next examination must be completed;

(l)   other observations;

(m)   where the most recent examination due was postponed in accordance with regulation 9(7), the names of appropriate members of the competent person's and the user's/owner's organisation, the date of giving the relaxation and the new date by which the examination was to be completed;

(n)   date examination took place;

(o)   name and address of competent person;

(p)   signature; and

(q)   date of report.

# Action in case of imminent danger

*(1)    If the competent person carrying out an examination under the scheme of examination is of the opinion that the pressure system or part of the pressure system will give rise to imminent danger unless certain repairs or modifications have been carried out or unless suitable changes to the operating conditions have been made, then without prejudice to the requirements of regulation 9, he shall forthwith make a written report to that effect identifying the system and specifying the repairs, modifications or changes concerned and give it -*

*(a)    in the case of an installed system, to the user; or*

*(b)    in the case of a mobile system, to the owner and to the user, if any,*

*and the competent person shall within 14 days of the completion of the examination send a written report containing the same particulars to the enforcing authority for the premises at which the pressure system is situated.*

*(2)    Where a report is given in accordance with paragraph (1) to -*

*(a)    the user of a pressure system, he shall ensure that the system (or, if the report only affects a discrete part of the system, that part) is not operated;*

*(b)    the owner of a mobile system, he shall take all reasonably practicable steps to ensure that the system (or, if the report only affects a discrete part of the system, that part) is not operated,*

*until the repairs, modifications or changes, as the case may be, have been carried out or made.*

*(3)    Where the competent person referred to in paragraph (1) is the user (in the case of an installed system) or owner (in the case of a mobile system) the requirement in that paragraph to give the report to the user or owner shall not apply, and the reference in paragraph (2) to the giving of the report to the user or owner shall be construed as a reference to the making of the report by him.*

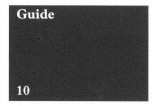

**Guide**

**10**

145   This regulation applies only to serious defects requiring immediate attention. That is, where there is a risk of imminent failure of the system if immediate repairs are not undertaken or other suitable modifications are not made to the operating conditions. The word 'forthwith' is used in the regulation to indicate that the competent person should notify the user/owner immediately so that appropriate action can be taken to prevent danger.

146   The user/owner should be notified immediately of those defects which the competent person considers could cause imminent failure of the system. Therefore, the written report to the user/owner should be made immediately. It is separate from and does not replace the report of the examination under the written scheme of examination required by regulation 9.

147   Competent person's reports are a vital diagnostic aid to the safe operation of pressure equipment. Defects which are identified only as a result of the competent person's examination, rather than as a result of checks under the maintenance regime, can point to failings in the general management of the system. Although the particular fault may be rectified immediately it is identified, the competent person should complete the report to the user/owner and relevant enforcing authority as detailed below.

148 Notification to the enforcing authority (ie the Health and Safety Executive or the Environmental Health Department of the Local Authority) is also a separate action required of the competent person. The period of 14 days to make this report to the enforcing authority is to allow sufficient time for a formal written report to be sent.

149 If the competent person is not clear about who is the relevant enforcing authority for a particular premises, they should contact the nearest HSE office for advice (the address will be in the local phone directory).

150 The sequence of events for reporting imminent danger is given below:

(a) The competent person immediately produces a written report identifying the system and specifying the repairs, modifications or changes required and gives it to the user/owner.

(b) The user/owner ensures that the system (or, if the report only affects a discrete part of the system, that part) is not operated until the necessary repairs, modifications or changes have been carried out.

(c) The competent person sends a written report to the relevant enforcing authority within 14 days.

(d) The competent person produces a report of the examination under the written scheme (regulation 9) and sends it to the user/owner within 28 days.

# Operation

*(1) The user of an installed system and the owner of a mobile system shall provide for any person operating the system adequate and suitable instructions for -*

*(a) the safe operation of the system; and*

*(b) the action to be taken in the event of any emergency.*

*(2) The user of a pressure system shall ensure that it is not operated except in accordance with the instructions provided in respect of that system under paragraph (1)(a).*

151 Although the provision of training to persons who use pressure systems is not covered by this regulation, it is required by regulation 9 of The Provision and Use of Work Equipment Regulations 1998. Those Regulations place a duty on the employer to ensure that anyone using work equipment, or supervising/managing its use, should have received adequate training for the purposes of health and safety.

152 The instructions provided to operators by the user/owner should cover:

(a) all procedures and information needed so that the system can be operated safely; and

(b) any special procedures to be followed in the event of an emergency.

153 Information provided by manufacturers or suppliers such as instruction sheets and operating manuals may form part or all of the instructions developed to meet these Regulations. To fulfil this role they

should be sufficiently comprehensive, cover the particular installation and its safe operation and be consistent with the site operating conditions.

154 The operator should be familiar with and have ready access to all the instructions. Instructions should be presented in the most appropriate way, eg simple, concise instructions may be displayed near the relevant part of the system. These should be pointed out to the operator before they use it for the first time.

155 Where a system is leased, the owner should provide all necessary instructions to the user. The user should ensure that the system is only operated in accordance with the instructions.

**Content**

156 The instructions should contain all the information needed for the safe operation of the system including:

(a)    start-up and shutdown procedures;

(b)    precautions for standby operation;

(c)    function and effect of controls and protective devices;

(d)    likely fluctuations expected in normal operation;

(e)    the requirement to ensure that the system is adequately protected against overpressure at all times; and

(f)    procedures in the event of an emergency.

157 The following paragraphs give more detailed guidance on the contents of instructions for particular types of systems:

**Steam and pressurised hot water plant**

158 Pre-firing and start-up instructions should include:

(a)    methods of establishing the proper water level in the boiler and maintaining adequate water supplies;

(b)    methods of carrying out any necessary flue gas side purging;

(c)    methods of establishing correct firing conditions so that pressure/temperature are raised carefully, preventing undue thermal shock; and

(d)    procedures to avoid water hammer.

159 There should also be instructions covering:

(a)    feed water treatment, if appropriate;

(b)    safe blowdown of the boiler and any other part of the system requiring such treatment;

(c)    precautions to be taken when emptying the boiler, eg by allowing it to cool down sufficiently before emptying it;

(d) precautions to ensure positive isolation and depressurisation of one boiler from a common header and blowdown system if internal access is required (see also paragraph 160);

(e) precautions to be taken before carrying out maintenance operations. This will include the requirement to ensure that the system is normally depressurised before carrying out maintenance and that protective devices are not disconnected or isloated while the plant is operating; and

(f) procedures to be followed in the event of a shortage of water, bursting of tubes or other event requiring the boiler to be shut down.

160 Where internal access is required and the steam boiler is one of a range of two or more boilers, this will include the requirement to either:

(a) disconnect all inlets through which steam or hot water might enter the boiler from any part of the range; or

(b) close and securely lock all valves or taps controlling the entry of steam or hot water. Where the boiler has a blow-off pipe in common with one or more other boilers or delivers into a common blow-off vessel or sump, it should only be possible to open the blow-off valve or tap on each boiler with a key which cannot be removed until the valve or tap is closed. There should only be one key in use for that set of blow-off valves or taps.

**Compressed air systems**

161 The instructions should cover at least all of the following items relevant to the particular system:

(a) checking and topping up of compressor lubricants;

(b) draining of receivers, intercoolers, aftercoolers, pipework etc;

(c) need for good housekeeping, in particular where dirt and/or spillage may affect the operation of or obscure any protective devices;

(d) warnings of the dangers associated with the removal of inspection covers or pipework before residual pressure has been vented; and

(e) thorough cleaning of receivers at the time of examination.

**Vessels with quick-opening or bolted access doors**

162 Instructions for vessels with quick-opening or bolted doors for access during a process cycle should include:

(a) information on the dangers of forcing the doors into position and of bypassing or interfering with door mechanisms;

(b) checks on door locking mechanisms in the open and closed positions;

(c) tightening and releasing the securing bolts of multi-bolted doors; and

(d)  checking that venting is complete before attempting to disengage the door-securing mechanism.

163  It is good practice to prepare a schematic circuit or flow diagram for the system, including pipework. The diagram should include all significant controls, valves and relevant safe operating limits with those of importance in an emergency clearly identified. Its purpose is to provide an easily accessible 'picture' of how the system is operated and controlled and to aid identification of the system's parts. It should be updated when changes are made to the system and be kept with the operating instructions.

164  The instructions should state that equipment should be depressurised before maintenance or other such tasks are carried out, thus avoiding the need to disconnect or isolate protective devices while the plant is in use. Only in very exceptional cases where plant cannot be depressurised should it be necessary to isolate or disconnect protective devices. In those very exceptional circumstances, adequate alternative arrangements are required to ensure that the system is fully protected against overpressure at all times. These arrangements should be detailed in the operating instructions. The following examples, while not exhaustive, detail precautions which should be taken before pressure-relieving devices are isolated from the vessels that they are designed to protect:

**Multiple pressure relief devices**

When isolating any one relief device for testing or servicing, ensure that the remaining relief device(s) connected to the vessel provides the full capacity required.

**Single pressure relief devices**

Where provision is made for removal of the valve for testing or servicing by the use, for example, of an automatic shut-off valve, a replacement relief device should be fitted immediately to ensure that the vessel is not left unprotected.

**Simultaneous isolation of relief and pressure source**

Where the only source of pressure which could lead to an unsafe condition originates from an external source, this source should also be isolated from the vessel protected by the relief device.

# Maintenance

*The user of an installed system and the owner of a mobile system shall ensure that the system is properly maintained in good repair, so as to prevent danger.*

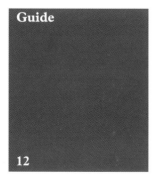

**Guide**

165  This regulation builds on the more general duties in the HSW Act and regulation 5 of the Provision and Use of Work Equipment Regulations 1998 which require that work equipment is maintained so that it does not give rise to risks to health and safety. The guidance on the Provision and Use of Work Equipment Regulations[4] contains information on maintenance management techniques.

166  The purpose of maintenance under this regulation is to ensure the safe operation and condition of the system. The actual process of carrying out the maintenance tasks is not covered. The risks associated with maintenance need

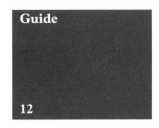

to be assessed to comply with the requirements of the Management of Health and Safety at Work Regulations 1999 and the appropriate precautions taken.

167 The need for maintenance should not be confused with the requirement for examinations under the written scheme. They are two separate issues although problems identified during an examination under the written scheme may require maintenance to correct.

168 **The type and frequency of maintenance for the system should be assessed and a suitable maintenance programme planned.**

169 **A suitable maintenance programme should take account of:**

(a)   **the age of the system;**

(b)   **the operating/process conditions;**

(c)   **the working environment;**

(d)   **the manufacturer's/supplier's instructions;**

(e)   **any previous maintenance history;**

(f)   **reports of examinations carried out under the written scheme of examination by the competent person;**

(g)   **the results of other relevant inspections (eg for maintenance or operational purposes);**

(h)   **repairs or modifications to the system; and**

(i)   **the risks to health and safety from failure or deterioration.**

170 Problems identified during operation of the system should be assessed for their impact on the safety of the system. For instance, recurrent discharge of a relief valve may indicate that the system or the relief valve are not working correctly and should be investigated as part of the planned maintenance regime. In processes where protective devices and other safeguards may become ineffective because of accumulations of deposits of process waste materials, frequent checks should be made to keep them in efficient working order. For example, in the case of digesters in by-product plants, regular checks should be made on the interlocking components and seals of doors to ensure that they operate correctly. Moving parts should be regularly lubricated and protective devices cleared of fatty deposits.

171 Where the manufacturer/supplier has provided maintenance instructions for all or part of the system, these should form the basis of the maintenance programme. They should be supplemented as appropriate where they are not sufficiently comprehensive to cover the particular installation. In assessing whether the manufacturer's/supplier's instructions are sufficient, account should be taken of the complexity of the system, whether they cover the particular installation and reflect the on-site operating conditions.

172 The type and frequency of maintenance tasks (inspections, replacement of parts etc) should be decided for all those parts which, through failure or malfunction, would affect the safe operation of the system. Although pipework systems may not always be included for

examination under the written scheme, checks and remedial action in potentially vulnerable areas such as expansion loops, bends, dead legs and low points or where leaks have been noticed will be necessary. Where appropriate, parts of systems should be checked during regular shutdowns when it may be easier to identify signs of deterioration such as leakage, external damage or corrosion, particularly if the equipment or pipework is lagged.

173 Systems which have been out of service for a significant period of time will need detailed checks and maintenance before being returned to service, irrespective of any examinations carried out under the written scheme.

**Instructions**

174 Instructions for maintenance staff should be readily available. The method used to provide staff with instructions will depend on the complexity of the system and the user's organisational arrangements. For example, a simple maintenance schedule could take the form of a checklist displayed near to the system. The aim should be to select the most appropriate method, taking into account all the relevant factors.

175 The extent and complexity of maintenance can vary substantially from simple checks on basic equipment to integrated programmes for complex plant. Checks will be necessary to ensure that safety-related features are operating correctly. A fault affecting production is normally apparent within a short time whereas a fault in a safety critical part, such as a protective device, could remain undetected unless appropriate safety checks are included as part of the maintenance programme.

176 Maintenance work to improve plant efficiency, reduce fuel consumption or for other production process reasons is not covered. It may, however, be convenient to implement a maintenance regime which combines both safety-related and operational maintenance tasks in one complete maintenance programme for the system.

# Modification and repair

*The employer of a person who modifies or repairs a pressure system at work shall ensure that nothing about the way in which it is modified or repaired gives rise to danger or otherwise impairs the operation of any protective device or inspection facility.*

177 The dutyholder for this regulation is the employer of the person engaged to carry out the repair or modification.

178 When designing any modifications (including extensions or additions) or repairs to the pressurised parts of the system, whether temporary or permanent, the following should be taken into account:

(a) the original design specification;

(b) the duty for which the system is to be used after the repair or modification, including any change in relevant fluid;

(c) the effects any such work may have on the integrity of the pressure system;

(d)   whether the protective devices are still adequate; and

(e)   continued suitability of the written scheme of examination.

179   Repair or modification of non-pressure containing parts of the system should be carried out so that the integrity of the pressure system is not adversely affected. This should ensure that any repairs, modifications (including extensions or additions) do not affect the operation of any protective devices.

180   Any repair or modification (including extensions or additions) should be designed in accordance with appropriate standards, taking into account the expected future duty of the system as well as the original design specification. It should be done by a person competent to do such work.

181   Where substantial modifications or repairs (including extensions or additions) are to be carried out which might increase the risk of system failure, the user should consult a person who is competent to advise before work begins.

# Keeping of records etc

*(1)   The user of an installed system and the owner of a mobile system shall keep -*

*(a)   the last report relating to the system made by the competent person pursuant to regulation 9(3);*

*(b)   any such previous reports if they contain information which will materially assist in assessing whether -*

*(i)    the system is safe to operate, or*

*(ii)   any repairs or modifications to the system can be carried out safely;*

*(c)   any -*

*(i)    information provided pursuant to regulation 5 of these Regulations; or*

*(ii)   instructions specified in section 3.4 of Annex I to Directive 97/23/EC of the European Parliament and of the Council on the approximation of the laws of the Member States concerning pressure equipment[(a)], which Annex is set out in Schedule 2 to the Pressure Equipment Regulations 1999[(b)], and provided pursuant to regulation 7(1) and (3) or 8(1) and (3)(b)(i) of those Regulations,*

*which relate to those parts of the pressure system included in the scheme of examination; and*

*(d)   any agreement made pursuant to regulation 9(7), and, in a case to which regulation 9(8) applies, a copy of the notification referred to in regulation 9(7)(c), until a further examination has been carried out since that agreement or notification under the scheme of examination.*

*(2) Anything required to be kept by this regulation shall be kept -*

*(a) in the case of an installed system, at the premises where the system is installed, or at other premises approved for the purposes of this sub-paragraph by the enforcing authority responsible for enforcing these Regulations at the premises where the system is installed;*

*(b) in the case of a mobile system, at the premises in Great Britain from which the deployment of the system is controlled;*

*(c) in a case to which regulation 2(2) applies, by means whereby it is capable of being reproduced as required by regulation 2(2)(a) at the premises referred to in sub-paragraph (a) or (b) as appropriate.*

*(3) Where the user or owner of a pressure system or part thereof changes, the previous user or owner shall as soon as is practicable give to the new user or owner in writing anything (relating to the system or part thereof, as the case may be) kept by him under this regulation.*

*(a) O.J. No. L181, 9.7.97, p.1.*
*(b) S.I. 1999/2001.*

182 Records retained should assist the competent person in the examination under the written scheme, the purpose being to assess whether the system is safe for continued use and/or if any planned repairs or modifications can be carried out safely.

183 The user/owner should keep the following documents readily available:

(a) any designer's/manufacturer's/supplier's documents relating to parts of the system included in the written scheme;

(b) any documents required to be kept by the Pressure Equipment Regulations 1999;

(c) the most recent examination report produced by the competent person under the written scheme of examination;

(d) any agreement or notification relating to postponement of the most recent examination under the written scheme; and

(e) all other reports which contain information relevant to the assessment of matters of safety.

184 In deciding whether a report contains relevant information, the user/owner should take account of the content of the report, the system's complexity, the operating conditions, previous history of repair and any significant modifications to the system.

185 Records of abnormal or particularly arduous operating conditions should be kept if they will be of use to the competent person at the next examination.

186 Where the owner/user is unsure whether certain records are relevant, the competent person should be asked to advise.

187 To avoid confusion, the records should be kept in such a way that it is possible to identify the particular system or parts of the system easily against those detailed in the written scheme of examination.

188 Where a system is sold or otherwise changes hands, the previous user/owner has a duty to pass all documents held under this regulation to the new user/owner. In this way, valuable information about the equipment's past history can be made available to those people who will be responsible for the system.

189 Examination reports and the written scheme of examination may be kept in hard copy form, stored electronically or on computer disc. If a computer system is used to keep this information then it must be able to reproduce it as a written copy when necessary, for example to an inspector from the relevant enforcing authority. It should be protected from unauthorised alteration and be authenticated only by the competent person who carried out the examination.

# Precautions to prevent pressurisation of certain vessels

*(1)    Paragraph (2) shall apply to a vessel -*

*(a)    which is constructed with a permanent outlet to the atmosphere or to a space where the pressure does not exceed atmospheric pressure; and*

*(b)    which could become a pressure vessel if that outlet were obstructed.*

*(2)    The user of a vessel to which this paragraph applies shall ensure that the outlet referred to in sub-paragraph (a) of paragraph (1) is at all times kept open and free from obstruction when the vessel is in use.*

190 The purpose of this regulation is to prevent an unintentional build-up of pressure in a vessel which is provided with a permanent outlet to atmosphere, or to a space where the pressure does not exceed atmospheric pressure.

191 This operating requirement applies principally to steam plant. However, other processes may have a similar operating requirement. For example, in the chemical industry where a reactor vessel is provided with a vent to atmosphere it may be necessary to keep the vent clear of obstruction to ensure that the reaction proceeds at or near atmospheric pressure. If the outlet becomes blocked with deposits or otherwise, the temperature in the reactor could build up to a point where control of the process is lost, the contents decompose, the vessel becomes overpressurised and then fails.

**PART III MISCELLANEOUS**

# Defence

*(1)    In any proceedings for an offence for a contravention of any of the provisions of these Regulations it shall, subject to paragraphs (2) and (3), be a defence for the person charged to prove -*

*(a)    that the commission of the offence was due to the act or default of another person not being one of his employees (hereinafter called "the other person"); and*

*(b)    that he took all reasonable precautions and exercised all due diligence to avoid the commission of the offence.*

(2)    The person charged shall not, without the leave of the court, be entitled to rely on the defence referred to in paragraph (1) unless, within a period ending seven clear days -

(a)    before the hearing to determine mode of trial, where the proceedings are in England or Wales;

(b)    before the intermediate diet, where the proceedings are summary proceedings in Scotland; or

(c)    before the first diet, where the proceedings are solemn proceedings in Scotland,

he has served on the prosecutor a notice in writing giving such information identifying or assisting in the identification of the other person as was then in his possession.

(3)    Where a contravention of this regulation by any person is due to the act or default of some other person, that other person shall be guilty of the offence which would, but for any defence under this regulation available to the first-mentioned person, be constituted by the act or default.

## Regulation 17

# Power to grant exemptions

(1)    Subject to paragraph (2), the Executive may, by a certificate in writing, exempt any person or class of persons or any type or class of pressure system from the application of any of the requirements or prohibitions imposed by these Regulations, and any such exemption may be granted subject to conditions and to a limit of time, and may be revoked by a certificate in writing at any time.

(2)    The Executive shall not grant any such exemption unless, having regard to the circumstances, and in particular to -

(a)    the conditions, if any, which it proposes to attach to the exemption; and

(b)    any other requirement imposed by or under any enactment which apply to the case,

it is satisfied that the health and safety or persons who are likely to be affected by the exemption will not be prejudiced in consequence of it.

## 17

## Regulation 18

# Repeals and revocations

(1)    Sections 34 to 38 of the Factories Act 1961[a] are repealed.

(2)    The Pressure Systems and Transportable Gas Containers Regulations 1989[b], regulation 21(6) of and Schedule 6 to the CDGCPL Regulations and regulation 3 of and Schedule 2 to the Carriage of Dangerous Goods (Amendment) Regulations 1999[c] are revoked.

(a) 1961 c. 34.
(b) S.I. 1989/2169.
(c) S.I. 1999/303.

## 18

## Regulation 19

# Transitional provision

The substitution of provisions in these Regulations for provisions of the Pressure Systems and Transportable Gas Containers Regulations 1989 shall not affect the continuity of the law; and accordingly anything done under or for the purposes of such provision of the 1989 Regulations shall have effect as if done under or for the purposes of any corresponding provision of these Regulations.

## PART I

## Schedule 1

# Pressure systems excepted from all regulations

**Regulation 3(2)**

*These Regulations shall not apply to -*

1    *A pressure system which forms part of the equipment of -*

    (a)    *a vessel used in navigation;*

    (b)    *a spacecraft, aircraft, hovercraft or hydrofoil.*

2    *A pressure system which forms part of, or is intended to form part of, a weapons system.*

3    *A pressure system which forms part of any braking, control or suspension system of a wheeled, tracked or rail mounted vehicle.*

4    *That part of a system which is only a pressure system because it is -*

    (a)    *subject to a leak test (except that this sub-paragraph shall not apply to a pipeline);*

    (b)    *pressurised unintentionally, such pressurisation being not reasonably foreseeable; or*

    (c)    *a pipeline pressurised by a relevant fluid solely as part of a test or line clearance operation, but this exception shall not apply if the pipeline -*

        (i)    *is used for the conveyance of a relevant fluid, or*

        (ii)    *is pressurised beyond its safe operating limits.*

5    *Any pipeline and its protective devices in which the pressure does not exceed 2 bar above atmospheric pressure (or 2.7 bar above atmospheric pressure if the normal pressure does not exceed 2 bar and the overpressure is caused solely by the operation of a protective device).*

6    *Any pressure system or part thereof which -*

    (a)    *is the subject of a research experiment; or*

    (b)    *comprises temporary apparatus being used in a research experiment,*

*if, in the case of regulations 4, 5, 6, 7, 11, 13 and 14, it is not reasonably practicable to comply with them.*

7    *Any plant or equipment required by regulation 6(3)(b) of the Diving at Work Regulations 1997*[a] *and used or intended to be used in the course of a diving project to which those Regulations apply.*

8    *A working chamber, tunnel, manlock or an airlock within which persons work in compressed air, being work to which the Work in Compressed Air Regulations 1996*[b] *apply.*

*(a) S.I. 1997/2776.*
*(b) S.I. 1996/1656.*

9    A tank to which the Carriage of Dangerous Goods By Rail Regulations 1996[a] or the Carriage of Dangerous Goods by Road Regulations 1996[b] apply.

10    Any pressure system being carried in a vehicle if the vehicle is engaged in an international transport operation within the meaning of the Convention concerning International Carriage by Rail[c] as revised or reissued from time to time (COTIF) and such carriage conforms in every respect either -

    (a)    to the provisions of the Uniform Rules concerning the Contract for International Carriage of Goods by Rail (CIM) which forms Appendix B to that Convention and to the regulations (RID) made thereunder; or

    (b)    to the conditions determined by an agreement relating to such carriage between the United Kingdom and another State under Article 5(2) of CIM.

11    Any pressure system being carried in a vehicle if the vehicle is registered outside the United Kingdom and the carriage is confined to Great Britain but nevertheless conforms with the provisions of the European Agreement concerning the international carriage of dangerous goods by road signed in Geneva on 30th September 1957 as revised or re-issued from time to time ("the ADR").

12    Any pressure system being carried in a vehicle if the vehicle -

    (a)    is engaged in an international transport operation within the meaning of the ADR;

    (b)    complies with the conditions contained in Annexes A and B to the ADR; and

    (c)    is certified pursuant to the ADR as complying with it,

or if the vehicle is engaged in a transport operation subject to a special bilateral or multilateral agreement to which Article 4 of the ADR refers and to which the United Kingdom is a Contracting Party.

13    Any pressure system being carried in a vehicle if the vehicle is engaged in an international transport operation within the meaning of Article 1(c) of the ADR , in accordance with regulation 3(1)(c)(ii) of the CDGCPL Regulations.

14    Any pressure system which is carried, or stored as goods in transit, as part of an international transport operation, if it complies with the appropriate provisions of the International Maritime Dangerous Goods Code issued by the International Maritime Organisation as revised or re-issued from time to time.

15    Any pressure system comprising a gas propulsion or a gas fired heating, cooking, ventilating or refrigerating system fitted to a motor vehicle or trailer (both within the meaning of section 185(1) of the Road Traffic Act 1998[d].

16    Any water cooling system on an internal combustion engine or on a compressor.

17    Any tyre used or intended to be used on a vehicle.

18    Any vapour compression refrigeration system incorporating compressor drive motors, including standby compressor motors, having a total installed power not exceeding 25 kW.

(a) S.I. 1996/2089.
(b) S.I. 1996/2095.
(c) Cmnd. 8535.
(d) 1998 c. 52.

*19    A mobile system of the type known as a slurry tanker, and containing or intended to contain agricultural slurry, and used in agriculture.*

*20    Prime movers including turbines.*

*21    Any pressure system which is an electrical or telecommunications cable.*

*22    Any pressure system containing sulphur hexafluoride gas and forming an integral part of high voltage electrical apparatus.*

*23    Any pressure system consisting of a water filled fluid coupling and used in power transmission.*

*24    Any portable fire extinguisher with a working pressure below 25 bar at 60°C and having a total mass not exceeding 23 kilogrammes.*

*25    Any part of a tool or appliance designed to be held in the hand which is a pressure vessel.*

**Guide**

192    Schedule 1 of the Regulations lists a number of general exceptions which significantly affect their application. Users/owners applying the Regulations are advised to consult Schedule 1, together with this guide, to determine what parts of the Regulations, if any, are relevant in the prevailing circumstances.

**Exceptions 1 and 2**

193    These exceptions cover systems which form part of the equipment of a ship. Also covered are weapons systems, and any aircraft or similar craft.

**Exception 3**

194    The Regulations do not cover pressure systems which form part of the braking, control or suspension system of road or rail vehicles. No internal combustion engine is considered to be covered by the Regulations.

**Exception 4**

195    A system which is only a pressure system because it is subject to a leak test is not covered by the Regulations. For example, radiators under leak test would be exempt. For definition of 'leak test' and other forms of pressure testing, refer to HSE Guidance Note GS4 *Safety in pressure testing*.[5]

196    The exception also covers situations where pressurisation is unintentional and not reasonably foreseeable. This is not a blanket exception to cover situations where the hazard should have been foreseen but was not. Proper enquiry is necessary to determine the safe operating limits when new plant or processes are developed. Protective measures should be designed into the plant if loss of process control can lead to excess pressure generation within the system.

197    Also exempt from the Regulations are pipelines normally used for conveyance of liquids but which are pressurised solely as part of a test or line clearance operation.

**Exception 5**

198    The definition of a pressure system includes 'a pipeline containing a relevant fluid'. This exception excludes from the Regulations low pressure gas distribution pipelines provided that -

(a) the operating pressure does not exceed 2 bar above atmospheric pressure; and

(b) a protective device prevents the pressure from exceeding a maximum of 2.7 bar above atmospheric pressure in the event of a temporary pressure excursion occurring.

**Exception 6**

199 Where pressurised apparatus has been set up in a laboratory and is itself the subject of a research experiment, it may not be reasonably practicable to apply most of the regulations to the equipment. In the case of other research projects the individual circumstances and duration of the project will dictate whether it is reasonably practicable to comply with the Regulations. However, anyone relying on this exception should be able to justify their reasons for non-compliance and any failure to take the basic precautions required under the Regulations to prevent risk of injury from system failure.

**Exception 7**

200 Plant and equipment used in diving projects is already the subject of requirements under the Diving at Work Regulations 1997. Plant and equipment required by regulation 6(3)(b) of those Regulations are excepted from the Pressure Systems Safety Regulations 1999. The wording 'intended to be used' is inserted to extend the exception to manufacturer's premises where the diving equipment may be under test.

**Exception 8**

201 The Regulations do not apply to any working chamber, tunnel, manlock or airlock in which people work in compressed air and which are covered by the Work in Compressed Air Regulations 1996. If pressure systems such as mobile compressors and air receivers are provided on the surface or are taken into the working chamber, tunnel, manlock or airlock for work activities, then these pressure systems fall within the scope of the Pressure Systems Safety Regulations 1999.

**Exception 9**

202 A road tanker or tank container is exempt from the provisions of these Regulations while the Carriage of Dangerous Goods by Road Regulations 1996 apply. This should prevent overlapping requirements. However, if the tank or tank container ceases to be subject to those Regulations, the Pressure Systems Safety Regulations will apply when a relevant fluid is carried. But examinations of vessels carried out under the Carriage of Dangerous Goods by Road Regulations 1996 will be acceptable as providing compliance with the relevant requirements in the Pressure Systems Safety Regulations. (See also paragraph 218.)

203 It should be noted that certain pressurised tankers containing non-hazardous materials which are not subject to the Carriage of Dangerous Goods by Road Regulations 1996 will be mobile systems under the Pressure Systems Safety Regulations and will need to be examined accordingly.

**Exceptions 10, 11, 12, 13 and 14**

204 These exceptions relate to international road, rail and sea transportation involving a pressure system. Broadly, such international transport operations are exempt from the provisions of the United Kingdom Regulations if full

compliance is achieved with the relevant international agreements, which have broadly similar objectives to UK legislation. To be exempt, however, the transport operation has to be international, ie the consignment concerned has to be on an international journey which begins or ends abroad.

### Exception 15

205  This provision exempts from the Regulations the fuel storage tank and fuel system of a vehicle which uses a relevant fluid for propulsion and also exempts other pressure systems found on a vehicle such as those for heating, cooking, ventilation and refrigeration.

### Exception 16

206  This paragraph confirms the exception of pressurised water cooling systems both for internal combustion engines and compressors. The Regulations do not apply to a pressure system which is part of a braking, control or suspension system of a vehicle (exception 3) or to prime movers which are pressure vessels (exception 20).

### Exception 17

207  The exception clause for tyres has been inserted to make it clear that a tyre should not be considered a rigid vessel, and so brought within the scope of the Regulations.

### Exception 18

208  This exception excludes small refrigeration systems from the Regulations.

### Exception 19

209  The exception for slurry tankers relates only to those tankers which are used in agriculture.

### Exception 20

210  This exception disapplies the Regulations to prime movers, which includes turbines and prime movers of steam locomotives. The exception would also cover pressurised pit support systems used in the mining industry.

### Exception 21

211  Some electrical and telecommunications systems incorporate cables which are pressurised with air in excess of 0.5 bar above atmospheric pressure. Such cables are not to be treated as part of a pressure system as defined. However, some systems incorporate a compressor and conventional air receiver and the Regulations will apply to that part of the pressure system.

### Exception 22

212  Certain types of switchgear forming part of high-voltage electrical apparatus containing sulphur hexafluoride gas are covered by a specific exception. This type of equipment is manufactured for long service; it is not intended to be opened up and internal examination might increase the risk of electrical failure in service.

**Exception 23**

213 Water-filled fluid couplings are used extensively for conveyor systems subject to very heavy duty such as in mines. Under certain circumstances, steam can be generated in them, and larger couplings would then be subject to these Regulations unless excepted. Such couplings, which are not constructed as pressure vessels, are invariably fitted with suitable protective devices to prevent system failure, and the requirements of the Regulations are inappropriate.

**Exception 24**

214 Portable fire extinguishers manufactured as pressure vessels (ie not transportable pressure receptacles) are excluded from the Regulations if they have a working pressure below 25 bar (gauge) at 60°C, and have a total mass not exceeding 23 kilogrammes. However, fixed (installed) fire extinguishing systems containing a relevant fluid are subject to the Regulations as a pressure system.

**Exception 25**

215 Hand-held tools which otherwise might be considered as pressure vessels, and therefore covered by the Regulations, are excepted provided that the hand-held part of the tool contains the pressure vessel. This exception would mostly apply to small, compressed air-driven tools. Tools where the pressure vessel is not part of the hand-held portion (such as steam strippers where the steam is generated in a tank) are not excepted from these Regulations.

PART II

# Pressure systems excepted from certain regulations

Schedule

*1    Regulations 4 and 5(1) and (4) shall not apply to -*

*(a)    pressure systems to which the Medical Devices Regulations 1994[a] apply, other than those which contain or are liable to contain steam; or*

*(b)    pressure equipment or assemblies within the meaning of the Pressure Equipment Regulations 1999 to which regulation 7(1), 8(1), 9(1) or 10 of those Regulations apply.*

*2    (1)    Subject to sub-paragraph (2), regulations 5(4), 8 to 10 and 14 shall not apply to a pressure system containing a relevant fluid (other than steam) if the product of the pressure in bar and internal volume in litres of its pressure vessels is in each case less than 250 bar litres.*

*(2)    Until 21st August regulations 8 to 10 and 14 shall not apply to a pressure system brought into operation before the coming into force of these Regulations if the product of the pressure in bar and internal volume of its pressure vessel with the largest internal volume is less than 250 bar litres.*

*3    Regulations 4, 5, 7 to 10, 13 and 14 shall not apply to a tank container if -*

*(a)    it is intended to be used in the carriage of dangerous goods to which the Carriage of Dangerous Goods by Road Regulations 1996 apply, or would apply but for an exception specified in paragraph 1 of Schedule 2 thereof and is present solely for the purpose of being loaded with the goods to be carried; or*

*(b)    it has been used in such carriage, has been temporarily removed from a vehicle and is present solely for the purpose of unloading the goods from it.*

*(a) S.I. 1994/3017.*

1

Guide

## Exception 1

216    Pressure equipment which is subject to the Pressure Equipment Regulations 1999 (PER) is excepted from regulations on design, construction and provisions for information and marking. One example of equipment not covered by this exception is systems containing steam at a pressure of 0.5 bar (gauge) or less.

## Exception 2

217    This exception relates only to pressure systems containing a relevant fluid other than steam where the product of the pressure (in bars) and the internal volume (in litres) in each vessel in the system is less than 250 bar litres. Where the relevant fluid is steam all the regulations apply, irrespective of the vessel pressure and size.

## Exceptions 3 and 4

218    These exceptions have been inserted to ensure that tank containers subject to the Carriage of Dangerous Goods by Road Regulations 1996 and examined under the provisions of those Regulations are not subject to the corresponding provisions of the Pressure Systems Safety Regulations when they have been removed from a vehicle. However, the operational provisions of the Pressure Systems Safety Regulations will continue to apply.

Schedule 1

# Modification of duties in cases where pressure systems are supplied by way of lease, hire, or other arrangements

**Regulation 3(5)**

1 (a) *This paragraph applies where a person supplies an installed system by way of lease or hire, and agrees in writing to be responsible for discharging the duties of the user under all the provisions of regulations 8(1) and (2), 9(1), 11(1), 12 and 14.*

 (b) *During such time as the agreement is in force the supplier shall discharge the duties of the user under the said provisions.*

 (c) *It shall be a defence in any proceedings against the user of an installed system -*

  (i) *for an offence for a contravention of any of the said provisions; or*

  (ii) *in any civil proceedings for breach of duty (mentioned in section 47(2) of the 1974 Act) imposed by any such provisions,*

  (iii) *for that person to prove that the supplier had agreed in writing to be responsible for discharging the user's duty at the relevant time.*

 (d) *During such time as the agreement is in force the following provisions of this paragraph shall have effect.*

 (e) *Where the competent person who is to carry out the examination under the scheme of examination is a person other than the supplier, the supplier shall notify the competent person that any reports required to be sent or given to the user under regulation 9(3) or 10(1) shall be sent or given to the supplier as well.*

 (f) *On being so notified under sub-paragraph (e) above, the competent person shall comply with regulations 9(3) and 10(1) as if the reference therein to sending or giving a report to the user also included a reference to sending or giving a report to the supplier.*

 (g) *On receipt of a report from a competent person under regulation 9(3) or 10(1) (or in the case where the supplier is also the competent person, on the making by him of that report) the supplier shall take all practicable steps to ensure that the pressure system will not be operated in contravention of regulation 9(6) or 10(2), as the case may be.*

 (h) *The references in regulation 9(7) (in both places where it appears) and 9(8) to the user shall be read as references to the supplier.*

 (i) *The reference in regulation 14(2)(a) to the premises where the system is installed shall be read as a reference to the premises in Great Britain where the leasing or hiring out of the system is controlled; except that this modification shall not apply to the application of that sub-paragraph to regulation 14(6)(a) where the competent person is using the procedure referred to in regulation 14(4) in relation to the sending of the report to the user.*

2 *Where a person supplies a pressure system to another ("the customer") under a hire-puchase agreement, conditional sale agreement, or lease, and -*

(a)    he carries on the business of financing the acquisition of goods by others by means of such agreements, or, if financing by means of leases, the use of goods by others;

(b)    in the course of that business he acquired his interest in the pressure system supplied to the customer as a means of financing its acquisition by that customer (or, in the case of a lease, its provision to that customer); and

(c)    in the case of a lease he or his agent either has not had physical possession of that pressure system, or has had physical possession of it only for the purpose of passing it on to the customer,

the customer and not the person who provided the finance shall be treated for the purpose of these Regulations as being the owner of the pressure system, and duties placed on owners in these Regulations shall accordingly fall on the customer and not on the person providing the finance.

3    Section 6(9) of the 1974 Act[a] and the Health and Safety (Leasing Arrangements) Regulations 1992[b] shall apply to these Regulations as they apply to the remainder of section 6 of that Act.

(a) Section 6(9) was amended by the Consumer Protection Act 1987 (c. 43) Schedule 3, paragprah 1(9).
(b) S.I. 1992/1524.

**Guide**

**Schedule 2**

219    This Schedule allows the supplier, in the case of a leased installed system, to assume responsibility in writing for compliance with those regulations which deal with written scheme examinations, operation, maintenance and record keeping. The Schedule, therefore, covers the supply of reports on those examinations conducted under the written scheme. As these Regulations do not apply to systems installed at domestic premises, reports do not have to be provided to users in such cases. However, where the user is self-employed and uses the pressure system in connection with work activity, copies of examination reports should be provided by the supplier to the user.

# Marking of pressure vessels

**Regulation 5(4) and (5)**

The information referred to in regulation 5(4) is as follows -

1    The manufacturer's name.

2    A serial number to identify the vessel.

3    The date of manufacture of the vessel.

4    The standard to which the vessel was built.

5    The maximum allowable pressure of the vessel.

6    The minimum allowable pressure of the vessel where it is other than atmospheric.

7    The design temperature.

# User/owner decision tree

**Do the Regulations apply to my pressure system?**

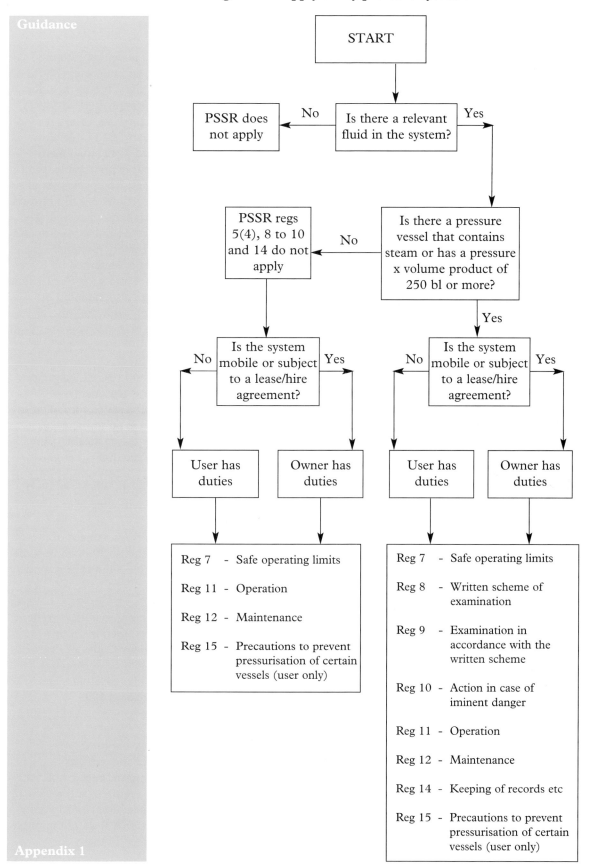

# Major health and safety legislation

(Note: this appendix does not form part of the Code)

## Health and Safety at Work etc Act 1974 (HSW Act)

1    This Act applies to everyone concerned with work activities, ranging from employers, to manufacturers, designers, suppliers and importers of materials for use at work, and people in control of premises. It also includes provisions to protect members of the public. The duties apply both to individual people and to corporations, companies, partnerships, local authorities, nationalised industries etc. The duties are expressed in general terms, so that they apply to all types of work activity and work situations. Every employer has a duty to ensure, so far as is reasonably practicable, the health, safety and welfare at work of his or her employees. The principles of safety responsibility and safe working are expressed in sections 2-9. Employers and self-employed are required to carry out their undertakings in such a way as to ensure, so far as is reasonably practicable, that they do not expose people who are not their employees to risks to their health and safety (sections 3(1) and 3(2)). In some areas the general duties have been supplemented by specific requirements in Regulations made under the Act and such Regulations will continue to be made. Specific legal requirements are also included in earlier legislation which is still in force. Failure to comply with the general requirements of the Act or specific requirements found elsewhere may result in legal proceedings.

2    Although some of the duties imposed by the Act and related legislation are absolute, many are qualified by the words 'so far as is reasonably practicable' or 'so far as is practicable'. If someone is prosecuted for failing to comply with a duty which is qualified by these words, it is up to the accused to show to the court that it was not reasonably practicable or practicable, as appropriate, to do more than was done to comply with the duty.

3    The judgement of what is reasonably practicable means weighing up the seriousness of the risk against the difficulty and cost of removing it.

4    Where the difficulty and cost are high and a careful assessment of the risk shows it to be insignificant, action may not be necessary although in some cases there are things that have to be done at all costs. No allowance is made for size, nature or profitability of a business.

5    Sections 21-23 provide for improvement and prohibition notices to be issued: section 33 provides for prosecution and penalties; section 15 provides for Regulations to be made; sections 16 and 17 provide for Codes of Practice to be approved and for their use in legal proceedings.

## Management of Health and Safety at Work Regulations 1999 (MHSWR)

6    The central feature of these Regulations is the duty imposed on employers and self-employed persons to make a suitable and sufficient assessment of risks to the health and safety of employees, and non-employees affected by their work. MHSWR also requires effective planning and review of protective measures, health surveillance, emergency procedures, information and training. The requirements in regulation 7(8) of MHSWR do not apply to the specific duties placed on competent persons as defined in these Regulations (PSSR).

## Workplace (Health and Safety) Regulations 1992 (WHSR)

7    These Regulations[6] impose requirements with respect to the health, safety and welfare of persons in a 'workplace' which, with certain exceptions, covers any premises or part of premises which are not domestic premises and are made available to any person as a place of work. This includes certain areas, eg staircases, lobbies and corridors used as a means of access to, or egress from a workplace or where facilities are provided for use in connection with the workplace, eg boiler/central heating plant rooms.

8    The Regulations include requirements for maintenance of the workplace and certain devices and systems, ventilation, temperature, lighting, cleanliness and other provisions. These requirements are imposed on employers, persons who have, to any extent, control of a workplace, and certain others.

## Provision and Use of Work Equipment Regulations 1998 (PUWER)

9    These Regulations impose health and safety requirements with respect to 'work equipment', which includes any machinery, appliance, apparatus or tool and certain assemblies of components. The requirements address the suitability of work equipment; maintenance and related records; inspection and associated records; measures to deal with specific risks (including use of designated persons to operate, repair, maintain and service equipment); information, instruction and training of users and others; and other specific areas (eg dangerous parts of machinery, protection from high and low temperature, lighting and stability of equipment).

10    The requirements apply to employers in respect of work equipment provided for, or used by, their employees for use at work. They also apply to self-employed persons and persons in control of work equipment to any extent.

## Confined Spaces Regulations 1997

11    Where a risk assessment undertaken under the Management of Health and Safety at Work Regulations 1999 identifies risks of serious injury from work in confined spaces, the Confined Spaces Regulations 1997 will apply.[7] These Regulations contain key duties to avoid entry to confined spaces or, where such entry is unavoidable, to follow a safe system of work and put in place adequate emergency arrangements before the work starts.

## Pipelines Safety Regulations 1996 (PSR)

12    These Regulations impose requirements on pipelines for purposes of health and safety. The requirements, with certain exceptions, cover any pipe or system of pipes for conveying fluids; this includes pipes supplying gas to premises (ie transmission pipes, distribution mains and service pipes) but excludes anything downstream of an emergency control, eg installation pipework, meters and other fittings, as covered by Gas Safety (Installation and Use) Regulations 1998. Any pipeline contained wholly within the premises occupied by a single undertaking, or contained wholly within a caravan site, is not covered by the Regulations.

13    The Regulations include requirements for design, construction, installation, examination and maintenance of pipelines, and for decommissioning of disused pipelines. Additional requirements are imposed in relation to certain ('major accident hazard') pipelines, including notification to HSE of specified information, preparation of a major accident prevention document and drawing up emergency procedures.

**Reporting of Injuries, Diseases and Dangerous Occurrences Regulations 1995 (RIDDOR)**

14    These Regulations require employers to report specified occupational injuries, diseases and dangerous events to HSE.

**Carriage of Dangerous Goods (Classification, Packaging and Labelling) and Use of Transportable Pressure Receptacles Regulations 1996 (CDGCPL2)**

15    These Regulations require anyone carrying dangerous goods by road or rail to protect the people involved in handling and carrying the goods, members of the emergency services and the public, as well as both property and the environment, from the potential dangers of such activities. The Regulations also contain special provisions for transportable pressure receptacles, covering their design, manufacture, supply, modification, repair, approval and certification, marking, filling and record keeping.

**References**

1    *A guide to the Health and Safety at Work etc Act* 1974 L1 HSE Books 1992 ISBN 0 7176 0441 1

2    *A guide to the Pipelines Safety Regulations 1996. Guidance on Regulations* L82 HSE Books 1996 ISBN 0 7176 1182 5

3    *Management of health and safety at work. Management of Health and Safety at Work Regulations 1999. Approved Code of Practice and Guidance* L21 (Second edition) HSE Books 2000 ISBN  0 7176 2488 9

4    *Safe use of work equipment. Provision and Use of Work Equipment Regulations 1998. Approved Code of Practice and Guidance* L22 (Second edition) HSE Books 1998 ISBN 0 7176 1626 6

5    *Safety in pressure testing* GS4 (Third edition) HSE Books 1998 ISBN 0 7176 1629 0

6    *Workplace health, safety and welfare. Workplace (Health Safety and Welfare) Regulations 1992. Approved Code of Practice and Guidance* L24 HSE Books 1992 ISBN 0 7176 1413 6

7    *Safe work in confined spaces. Confined Spaces Regulations 1997. Approved Code of Practice, Regulations and Guidance* L101 HSE Books 1997 ISBN 0 7176 1405 0

**Further reading**

*Essentials of health and safety at work* HSE Books 1994 ISBN 0 7176 0716 X

*Pressure systems safety and you* INDG261 HSE Books 1997 Single copies free, multiple copies in priced packs ISBN 0 7176 1452 2

*Written schemes of examination: Pressure Systems and Transportable Gas Containers Regulations 1989* INDG178 HSE Books 1994 Free publication

*Safe work in confined spaces* INDG258 HSE Books 1997 Single copies free, multiple copies in priced packs ISBN 0 7176 1442 5

*Automatically controlled steam and hot water boilers* PM5 HSE Books 1997 ISBN 0 7176 1028 4

*Steam boiler blowdown systems* PM60 HSE Books 1998 ISBN 0 7176 1533 2

*Safety at autoclaves* PM73 HSE Books 1998 ISBN 0 7176 1534 0

*Safe management of ammonia refrigeration systems* PM81 HSE Books 1995 ISBN 0 7176 1066 7

While every effort has been made to ensure the accuracy of the references listed in this publication, their future availability cannot be guaranteed.

British Standards are available from BSI Customer Services, 389 Chiswick High Road, London W4 4AL. Tel: 0208 996 9001 Fax: 0208 996 7001.

The Stationery Office (formerly HMSO) publications are available from The Publications Centre, PO Box 276, London SW8 5DT. Tel: 0870 600 5522 Fax: 0870 600 5533. They are also available from bookshops.